CH00660367

THE JURASSIC COAST
AN AERIAL JOURNEY THROUGH TIME

Editor Alison Moss
Design Jonathan Lewis
Publishing Manager Susan Sutterby

First Published in 2011 by Coastal Publishing this revised edition published in 2018
by the Jurassic Coast Trust
Jurassic Coast Trust
Rax Lane, Bridport, Dorset, DT6 3JP
Tel: 01308 807000
Email: info@jurassiccoast.org
www.jurassiccoast.org

© Jurassic Coast Trust 2018 – all rights reserved
Aerial photographs © Peter Sills
Text © Robert Westwood
Foreword © Denys Brunsden, OBE, DSc (Hons), FKC

ISBN 978-1-907701-02-3

British Library Cataloguing-in-Publication Data
A catalogue record for this book is available from the British Library.

All rights reserved. Except for the purpose of review, no part of this book may be reproduced, stored in
a retrieval system, or transmitted, in any form or by any means, electronic, mechanical, photocopying,
recording or otherwise, without the prior written permission of Jurassic Coast Trust.

Any views or opinions expressed in this publication are solely those of the author and do not necessarily
represent those of the publisher.

In the interests of your personal safety and enjoyment of the World Heritage Coast, the Jurassic Coast
Trust recommend that you follow fully all the relevant Safety, Fossil and Countryside codes. The Jurassic
Coast Trust can accept no liability whatsoever.

Proceeds from the sales of this book go to the The Jurassic Coast Trust (Registered Charity No: 1101134).
Your purchase supports our work to protect the Jurassic Coast and help anybody and everybody to love,
understand and value it. (Jurassic Coast Trust Registered charity: 1101134) Funds will be used to support
the conservation and education programmes for the Site. www.jurassiccoast.org

Printed and bound in UK

Image Acknowledgements

Images in this book are copyright of the photographers and artists.
All aerial photography was taken by Peter Sills. Other photography by Robert Westwood except South
Western Stone Company (1933): Portland Quarry, page 60; Richard Edmonds: dinosaur footprint, page
88; School of Earth & Environment, Leeds University: coccoliths, page 96; Paleomap Project: Paleomap
globe illustrations pages 15, 31 and 107; Jurassic Coast Trust: Time spiral illustration page 9, illustrated
by David Scammell; Lyme Regis Museum: Ichthyosaur skull, page 36.

With special thanks to Professor Denys Brunsden for all his help and support.

The Jurassic Coast Trust and the author have made every reasonable effort to locate, contact and
acknowledge copyright owners and wishes to be informed by any copyright owners who are not
properly identified and acknowledged so that we can make any necessary corrections.

This publication was first published in 2011 by Coastal Publishing Limited and the Jurassic Coast
Trust is grateful to Peter Sills and Coastal Publishing for their contribution to the World Heritage Site
conservation.

THE JURASSIC COAST
AN AERIAL JOURNEY THROUGH TIME

PHOTOGRAPHS BY PETER SILLS

WORDS BY ROBERT WESTWOOD

A Jurassic Coast Trust book

CONTENTS

CONTENTS

INTRODUCTION

The wonderful aerial pictures in this book record the Jurassic Coast at the start of the twenty-first century. The landscape has evolved over millions of years and will continue to evolve; photographs taken later on, even in our lifetimes, will show changes. The 95 miles (155 kilometres) of cliffs and beaches of the Jurassic Coast provide a fascinating history of the processes that have formed, contorted and shaped the rocks over 185 million years. Not only that; within the rocks, the rich variety of fossils provides us with many details of the evolution of life during the Mesozoic Era (the Triassic, Jurassic and Cretaceous Periods), when animal life began again, almost from scratch, evolving exotic species that inhabited new and varied environments as the supercontinent of Pangaea broke up under the strain of global tectonic forces.

This, basically, is the reason the Jurassic Coast was granted World Heritage status. It is an outstanding example of a landscape that represents major events in the history of the Earth, in terms of both the development of the geography and geology of the Earth's surface and the evolution of life.

This book takes the reader on a journey through time, from the start of the Triassic Period to the end of the Cretaceous Period, which marks the end of the era. It is hoped that the aerial photographs and accompanying text will aid an understanding of the different structures and rock types. Even for those familiar with the coast, the photographs will provide new perspectives that render the understanding of the underlying structure more accessible. The chapters and photographs run roughly west to east along the coast, but not strictly so; the chapters have been chosen to reinforce the idea that the geological history can be divided into a number of episodes, all with a common theme. Classifying the history like this mirrors the way we study the development of life. All living things are divided into various groups: phylum, class, order, genus and species to name a few. The landscape of the Jurassic Coast has developed over 250 million years to the present day, just as life has evolved over this time. More than ever we are aware that the Earth's crust is a constantly changing structure and it is clear that this has been an important, if not defining, factor in the way the living world has developed. Environments are constantly changing, providing the impetus for natural selection.

The power source behind this is heat from within the Earth, but it was only in the latter part of the twentieth century that scientists realised what an important part it played in determining geological processes. The new science of 'plate tectonics' was born (this is dealt with in more detail in Chapter 7). Along the Jurassic

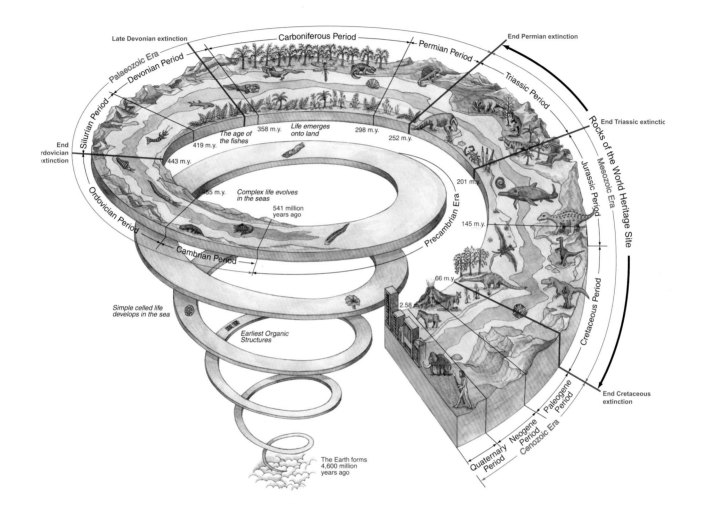

Late Devonian extinction

Carboniferous Period

End Permian extinction

Palaeozoic Era

Devonian Period

Permian Period

Silurian Period

Triassic Period

End Ordovician extinction

358 m.y.

The age of the fishes

Life emerges onto land

298 m.y.

252 m.y.

End Triassic extinction

419 m.y.

Rocks of the World Heritage Site

443 m.y.

Mesozoic Era

Ordovician Period

485 m.y.

Complex life evolves in the seas

201 m.y.

Jurassic Period

541 million years ago

Precambrian Era

145 m.y.

Cambrian Period

66 m.y.

Cretaceous Period

Simple celled life develops in the sea

2.58 m.y.

Earliest Organic Structures

End Cretaceous extinction

The Earth forms 4,600 million years ago

Neogene Period

Paleogene Period

Quaternary Period

Cenozoic Era

The time spiral

The spiral represents the evolving Earth over 4,500 million years. The rocks of the World Heritage Site cover the whole of the Mesozoic Era - the world of the reptiles, dinosaurs and the mammals.

Coast we see fascinating evidence of this intertwined evolution. As the various rock strata record the ever-changing environments of deposition, we can trace the development of creatures that exploited them. Based on our understanding of present habitats and the adaptations of animals that colonise them, we can draw conclusions about the ancient environments from the fossil remains, and about the lifestyles of the creatures now fossilised in the sediments.

As with other sciences, geology seems to get ever more complicated as more sophisticated techniques are used to research and analyse. This does not mean, however, that it is a discipline that is inaccessible to the layperson – far from it. The evolution of the Jurassic Coast is about how landscapes have changed and continue to change, what processes were and are involved, and how life has developed in these environments. It is a history open to all.

We begin the journey in East Devon, with red rocks from the start of the Triassic Period that were deposited in hot, arid deserts. At this time Britain was in tropical latitudes north of the Equator, in the middle of the supercontinent of Pangaea, which stretched from pole to pole. To the east the Tethys Ocean was spreading, a factor that would influence the development of the Jurassic Coast for many millions of years.

As we go eastwards along the coast we meet younger and younger rocks. In West Dorset we find early Jurassic marine sediments from a time when Britain had drifted further northwards and was near an east–west split that had developed in the great continent. As this split widened through the Jurassic Period and into the Cretaceous the upheavals resulted in Britain experiencing a variety of environments that are reflected in the sediments we find along the coast. Our journey is a fascinating exploration of these ancient environments.

Why does this matter? Well, for one thing, the East Devon and Dorset coast is a valuable educational resource for future geologists, and geology is a crucially important discipline if we are going to effectively and wisely use the Earth's resources for the good of all. But this is a very narrow and perhaps materialistic point of view; for those of us who delight in Nature's handiwork, a little understanding of the processes involved only adds to the enjoyment. Sites such as the Jurassic Coast are worth our efforts to preserve them for future generations, or, bearing in mind their continuing evolution, at least as long as we can! As Thomas Carlyle said: 'The man who cannot wonder, who does not habitually wonder (and worship)... is but a Pair of Spectacles behind which there is no Eye.'

Old Harry Rocks
The Chalk stacks of Old Harry near Studland are at the very eastern end of the Jurassic Coast. Chalk is the youngest rock on the World Heritage Site and dates from the last stage of the Cretaceous Period, which ended around 65 million years ago.

FOREWORD

In 2000 the Dorset and East Devon Coast was assessed for designation as a UNESCO World Heritage Site. The purpose was to examine the 'stories' that gave the site 'global universal value', deserving international recognition and a management plan that would look after it for all people. The site was inscribed in 2001 and three themes were recognised.

The 95 miles (155 kilometres) of the coast portrays in its rocks 185 million years of the history and evolution of the Earth. Because the rocks generally dip gently to the east successively younger rocks appear in the cliffs from Exmouth to Studland. This means that a walk from west to east along the beaches is a 'Walk Through Time' from the Triassic, through the Jurassic and into the Cretaceous Periods. This includes the whole of what geologists call the Mesozoic Era.

As this vast period of time passed, life forms evolved: plants, reptiles, dinosaurs, turtles, crocodiles, ammonites, fish, insects and mammals. They lived and died in deserts, shallow warm seas, hot swamps and deep oceans. Their remains were preserved in the rocks and are now found in rich profusion as current erosion washes them out of the cliffs. A walk through time along the coast now becomes 'a Walk Through the Evolution of Species'. What a wonderful story! A story which fully satisfied the criterion of the World Heritage Convention which asks for: 'Outstanding examples representing major stages of Earth's history, including the record of life...'

The specification also asked for evidence of 'significant on-going geological processes in the development of landforms or significant geomorphic or physiographic features'. The Dorset and Devon coasts have a spectacular array of landforms: remarkable cliffs, landslides, arches, stacks and beaches, especially the great landslides of Bindon, Black Ven or Stonebarrow and the iconic Chesil Beach and its enclosed lagoon, the Fleet. The story of the processes that shape the planet and tell the story of geomorphological and environmental change is one of our greatest educational opportunities.

Because these records are so clear and complete it is not surprising to discover that the features have been studied for over 200 years. Many great scientists, such as the Revd William Buckland, Professor of Mineralogy and Palaeontology at the University of Oxford, the Revd William Conybeare, Vicar at Axminster and Dean of Llandaff in Cardiff, or Sir Henry de la Beche, the founder of the Geological Survey of Great Britain, worked at Lyme Regis, which became one of the birthplaces of the geological sciences. Their example continues to this today.

Above all the coast became a Mecca for professional collectors like Mary Anning, amateur scientists, and the promoters of public science, school and university field trips and educational walks. Many of our best geologists and geomorphologists cut their teeth here.

Today most people see the coast from the cliffs and beaches or from sea level on a boat. A trip along the coast in a light aircraft or a helicopter is enjoyed by only a few professional or lucky people. This is a great shame, because it is only from the air that the full beauty and complexity of the coast can be comprehended. The author, Robert Westwood, and the photographer and designer of this volume therefore do us a great service by presenting this aerial view. The quality is superb and the perspectives new, rare and unusual. For the first time we can follow the extraordinary changes through space and time that make the World Heritage stories. The red desert rocks of East Devon, the blue-grey Jurassic marine sediments of West Dorset, the yellows of the Middle Jurassic deltas, the white limestones of the Upper Jurassic and Cretaceous in Portland and Purbeck.

Here too we see the shapes of the cliffs, beaches, landslides and bays that show the best examples in Britain of the relationships between rocks and the relief of the land. The aerial perspective also allows us to grasp how the rocks, structures and processes form the foundations for our soils, natural habitats, human settlements and land use.

The Jurassic Coast Trust is proud to be publishing this book, for it enables us to fulfil our mission to encourage the care of the coast and to educate everyone about its resources and values. The Trust believes that from education comes understanding. From understanding we gain respect. If we respect the coast, then we feel that it is important to us. If we feel we 'own' it, then we will look after it. May we encourage you to look deeply at the stories in this book and discover for yourselves the wonderful relationships of England's only natural World Heritage Site.

Professor Denys Brunsden OBE, DSc(Hons), FKC
Patron, Jurassic Coast Trust

CHAPTER 1 | THE GREAT DESERTS

It is now generally accepted that the continents of the Earth's crust have, from time to time, converged to form one giant 'supercontinent'. The last time this happened was at the end of the Palaeozoic era 250 million years ago, so our history of the Jurassic Coast begins, at the start of the Triassic Period, with the giant land mass of Pangaea (Greek for 'entire Earth') and its surrounding ocean dominating the surface of the planet. Pictures from orbiting satellites of this time would have shown a very different picture to the familiar shape of the continents we see today. The outline of the land would not have been all that was different; the vast interior of Pangaea would have been red, immediately recognisable as a bare, arid desert, with a thin strip of verdant green around the coastline. Impressive mountain ranges would, perhaps, also have shown signs of vegetation. There would have been no glistening white ice caps over the polar regions. Perhaps it would have appeared an inhospitable planet, but still it would have been obvious that life had a hold, however tenuous, around the edge of the great continent.

The interiors of large land masses generally have more extreme climates than areas closer to the oceans at the same latitude, creating hotter summers and colder winters. In Pangaea this effect would have been even more exaggerated. Some researchers have concluded that in the continental interior the average temperature may have fluctuated over 50°C between summer and winter. Although the interior was very dry, some regions probably had an intense monsoonal climate. The red rocks we now see on the coast of East Devon were formed in this harsh ancient environment.

As we walk along this now gentle landscape it is natural to question how we know such things about the Earth 250 million years ago: what is the evidence for this giant supercontinent? First, identical fossil assemblages are found of the same age in continents now widely separated, strongly suggesting that they were once together in the same environment. Likewise geological structures in different continents match up: for example, the mountain chains of the Appalachians in eastern North America and those of north-west Europe are part of the same system. Glaciers create striation marks on the rocks they glide over, leaving a record of their movement. When this is plotted on a map it shows how glaciers radiate from a central mountainous region. Traces from a very ancient glaciation show such a pattern when the continents are fitted together.

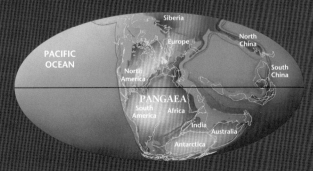

◄ *Looking east along the red Triassic cliffs from Orcombe Point, the start of the Jurassic Coast.*

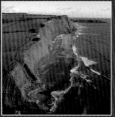

○ *Orcombe Point*

Page 14

○ *The Floors*

Page 17

○ *Budleigh Salterton*

Page 19

○ *The Otter Estuary*

Page 21

○ *Budleigh Salterton beach*

Page 23

○ *Ladram Bay*

Page 25

○ *Sidmouth*

Page 27

○ *Beer Head*

Page 29

Red cliffs west of Budleigh Salterton. ▶

THE BUDLEIGH SALTERTON PEBBLE BEDS

The Budleigh Salterton Pebble Beds provide a fascinating insight into ancient environments and how geologists can decipher the evidence for them. Extending up to 30 metres (100 feet) in thickness, these rocks are well displayed in the cliffs west of the charming town of Budleigh Salterton. The beds are made almost entirely of well-rounded pebbles of quartzite, a very hard sandstone. They lie on top of the Aylesbeare Mudstone, a rock formed in quiet, ephemeral desert lakes, and clearly represent a marked change in environment. It is thought the pebbles were carried by large, fast-flowing rivers from the south. They would have needed to flow at speeds fast enough to carry such a load, and the fact that the size of the pebbles diminishes as we trace the Pebble Beds northwards suggests that these rivers flowed from the south – the larger material would have been deposited first.

Quartzite is sandstone that has been metamorphosed; that is, it has been subjected to considerable pressure and high temperatures, which baked the original sandstone and fused the grains together into a much harder rock. This happens when tectonic plates are colliding and mountains are being pushed up from the sediment caught in between. The pebbles themselves sometimes contain fossils. These are not from the Triassic Period, when the Pebble Beds were being formed, but are much older, from the Ordovician and Devonian Periods. They have been matched with fossils of that age from Brittany, further evidence that the rivers came from the south. From what we know of the geology of Brittany, it seems that the rivers flowed from mountains of which Brittany and much of Cornwall are now the eroded core (there was no English Channel then). Thus we can imagine a flat desert with a mountainous region to the south from where powerful rivers suddenly began to bring vast amounts of gravel. The rivers seem to have stopped abruptly, at which point quieter conditions prevailed once more.

Pebbles on the beach at Budleigh Salterton.

Budleigh Salterton
The red cliffs west of Budleigh Salterton are largely composed of the well-known Budleigh Salterton Pebble Beds. Fast-flowing rivers from mountain regions brought their exotic pebbles on to the desert plains, spreading them over a wide region as the rivers meandered across the desert landscape.

THE OTTER ESTUARY

The River Otter rises in the Blackdown Hills of Somerset and flows through gentle, undulating farmland to the sea at Budleigh Salterton. The last part of the town's name dates from the Middle Ages when there were saltpans in the estuary. Nowadays 57 acres (23 hectares) of the salt marshes form the Otter Estuary Nature Reserve, a haven for many species of migrating birds and a Site of Special Scientific Interest.

The cliffs at Otterton Point to the east of the estuary are made from the Otter Sandstone, which is younger than and therefore overlies the Budleigh Salterton Pebble Beds. This desert sandstone was laid down partly by rivers and partly by wind. Such rocks are not noted for their fossils, as the action of rivers tends to break up animal remains and the chances of their being preserved are not good.

Nevertheless, some are found and the cliffs at Otterton Point have yielded a famous and very useful fossil of a rhynchosaur. Rhynchosaurs were reptiles that died out in the late Triassic, so finding one here confirms the rocks as Triassic. They were herbivores with small, compact bodies, perhaps a metre or so in length, and were distributed widely around Pangaea. They had very powerful jaws for cutting up and chewing vegetation. They are a good example of a fossil that helps correlate different rock strata around the world.

'Dear native Brook! wild streamlet of the West!' is how Samuel Taylor Coleridge, who was born in nearby Ottery St Mary, describes the river in his 'Sonnet to the River Otter'. His words are still applicable to this waterway, which, like much of the East Devon countryside, still charms and captivates the visitor.

But straight with all their tints thy waters rise,
Thy crossing plank, thy marge with willows grey,
And bedded sand that vein'd with various dyes
Gleam'd through thy bright transparence!

The beach at Budleigh Salterton.

The Otter Estuary
The Otter Estuary east of Budleigh Salterton is now a nature reserve and a Site of Special Scientific Interest. It is a haven for many bird species seeking refuge from colder climates. The estuary is now partly blocked by a spit of pebbles, its formation prompted by rising sea levels.

DEPOSITION IN DESERTS

We all have an idea what deserts are like even if we have never actually visited one. Cloudless skies, intense sun, sand dunes and little or no vegetation are all images that come to mind. Of course, the landscapes of real deserts vary widely; some are rocky and some are mountainous. All landscapes can be broadly categorised as regions where either erosion or deposition is taking place, and this is true of deserts. Some, in mountainous areas, are being eroded by the action of wind and sporadic, seasonal watercourses. In others, debris transported by wind or water is being deposited, gradually accumulating and hardening into new sedimentary rocks.

It is, perhaps, surprising to learn that water plays an important part in the formation of desert sediments, since deserts are, by definition, arid environments. Nevertheless, rain does fall and when it comes it is often sudden and severe. Rapid run-off can lead to ephemeral lakes in basins. Sand and silt that collected in such 'playa' (Spanish for 'beach') lakes in the Triassic Period form much of East Devon's red cliffs.

The meandering courses of seasonal rivers that descended from mountains to the south also deposited sediment that is seen on the Jurassic Coast of East Devon. These sandstones show the telltale stratification of current- or cross-bedding, formed as the course of a river changed and banks of sand sloping in different directions were laid on top of one another. Cross-bedding on a larger scale is also a feature of desert sands deposited by wind; dunes are pushed along by the wind, constantly changing position, again resulting in successive layers sloping in different directions.

Wind is a major factor in the erosion of desert surfaces. With little vegetation to bind the surface of the land, fine silt and dust are suspended in the air and may be carried great distances. Coarser sand particles are moved in a different way, being 'bounced' along the surface by the wind. There are some sandstones in the cliffs of the Red Coast that were deposited by wind. Such deposits are usually easy to recognise, as they consist almost entirely of quartz grains well rounded by abrasion during transport by the wind.

Cross-bedding in the Otter Sandstone.

Budleigh Salterton beach
At the top is Exmouth on the estuary of the River Exe, while in the centre is Budleigh Salterton. Along the coast you can see the red cliffs from the Triassic Period, sandstones formed in hot, arid deserts, most of them in temporary lakes or seasonal rivers.

STACKS AT LADRAM BAY

Few places on the South Devon coast have been photographed as much as Ladram Bay. Its stunning red cliffs and sea stacks have made it a popular place for visitors. The cliffs are of the Triassic Otter Sandstone, a desert rock formed by seasonal rivers and streams that flowed across the ancient, arid landscape around 240 million years ago. Look closely at the cliffs and you will see the characteristic cross-bedding created where river channels have meandered through the desert and cut across pre-existing channels.

It is the sea stacks that give the bay its unique character. These features are typically formed as waves erode headlands, cutting through and opening up arches, which subsequently collapse as erosion continues, leaving isolated stacks. Naturally this can only happen with certain types of rocks; soft sands and clays do not have the structural strength necessary to support arches, nor do they provide a stable wave-cut platform on which arches and stacks can stand.

You may have wondered why sea stacks are not common along the Red Coast, and why they have formed here at Ladram Bay. It may be because the rocks at Ladram Bay have been weakened by more faults and joints than elsewhere along the coast. The sea exploited these weaknesses, eroding along the joints and eventually cutting through. Faults and joints are planes of weakness in the rocks caused by tensional forces, which again are a result of the movement of the Earth's plates or of local readjustments of the crust to these movements. Joints are smaller in scale than faults, and faults typically show some relative movement between the rock either side. Fortuitously the stacks at Ladram Bay have a rather hard sandstone layer near the base, which protects them somewhat from the waves; nevertheless, stacks are a temporary feature and one day will be eroded away completely.

The cliffs and pebble beach at Ladram Bay.

Ladram Bay

Ladram Bay is a popular holiday destination with a picturesque, sheltered beach and prominent sea stacks eroded from the red Otter Sandstone. In this low-level picture, the almost horizontal layers in the sandstone can be clearly seen, including the relatively hard layer at the base of the cliffs (centre) which protects the stacks somewhat from erosion.

SIDMOUTH

Sidmouth is the classic English seaside town, with a long promenade, stylish Regency architecture and a gentle, languid atmosphere that compels you to relax and enjoy the sea air. That is not to say, however, that Sidmouth is living in the past. It is a thriving community with a world-famous folk festival that attracts thousands of visitors each year, and in the summer, when its many gardens are in full flower, it is easy to appreciate its appeal.

Sidmouth is flanked on either side of the wide valley of the River Sid by red sandstone cliffs from the Triassic Period. It is mentioned in the Domesday Book of 1086 and was originally a small fishing village, although attempts to create a harbour here have met with failure. It developed in Georgian and Victorian times when it became fashionable to holiday by the seaside, and many fine villas were built that still grace the esplanade, some of which have become luxury hotels.

The town museum near the parish church is set in a delightful Regency building and has some interesting collections on local history as well as an informative display about the Jurassic Coast. On nearby Salcombe Hill is the Norman Lockyer Observatory, founded by the scientist who is jointly credited with the discovery of helium in 1868. The observatory holds regular open days when members of the public can look round and view the night sky through the telescopes if conditions are right. It also runs many educational courses.

The town was a favourite destination for Poet Laureate John Betjeman, who included it in his book and television series about John Betjeman in the West Country. His description of Sidmouth as 'a town caught in a timeless charm' has been used many times by local businesses, but few would dispute that it still applies!

The foreground of the aerial photograph shows the impressive cliffs of Salcombe Hill, east of the town. These are the Mercia Mudstones, again formed in seasonal desert lakes. The red colour of the water below them is an indication of how serious coastal erosion is here.

View along the coast east of Sidmouth.

Sidmouth

Looking down on the charming seaside resort of Sidmouth with its famous esplanade and many gardens. The Norman Lockyer Observatory is on Salcombe Hill just to the east of the town and right of the picture. Notice the plumes of red sand in the sea, emphasising the transitory nature of the coastline. Erosion of the cliffs is a problem here, especially for the houses just to the east of the estuary of the River Sid.

THE COLOUR OF ROCKS

What makes a rock a particular colour? Rocks are collections of minerals, each of which has its own colour. Granite, an igneous rock, is composed of minerals fused together as they crystallised out of a molten state. Some of the constituents are white, some clear, dark or pink. The resulting rock has a mottled appearance, although light colours usually dominate. Basalt lava on the other hand consists mostly of dark-coloured minerals; the crystals are typically very small, so the rock presents as a uniform black. The rocks of the Jurassic Coast are all sediments, formed either from the weathering and subsequent deposition of material from older rocks or as chemical precipitates of calcium carbonate (limestones).

The red rocks of the Devon coast are largely sandstones. Sand grains are made from the most common material in the Earth's crust, silica, which is itself a compound of the two most common elements in the crust, oxygen and silicon. Quartz is a colourless mineral, while the red colour comes from the iron oxide that cements the grains of the sandstones together. The Devon sandstones were probably not originally such a bright red; this has occurred due to the change iron oxide undergoes when it is buried and heats up under pressure.

Limestones contain much calcium carbonate in the form of the mineral calcite. In some oceans there is a lot of this mineral dissolved in the seawater originating from the hard parts of dead organisms. In certain conditions it precipitates out, cementing bits of sand and other shell material together, eventually forming limestone. Calcite is colourless or white and limestones are often light-coloured because of this, although the presence of iron can again lead to a rich orange colour, as in the limestones around Abbotsbury and Osmington.

There is one rock on the Jurassic Coast which, in some places, is pure white. This is Chalk, which consists almost entirely of calcite derived from microscopic organisms.

Red sandstone cliffs at Budleigh Salterton.

Beer Head

The impressive Chalk cliffs of Beer Head in East Devon are slowly crumbling into the sea. Behind the headland is the sprawling Hooken landslip, formed one night in March 1790 when heavy rains lubricated the base of the Upper Greensand on which the Chalk rests. The colour of Chalk reflects the colour of the mineral calcite, which is its main constituent.

CHAPTER 2 | THE SEA RETURNS

The end of the Triassic Period and the beginning of the Jurassic Period 200 million years ago was marked by a rise in sea level, and areas that had previously been desert environments became shallow seas. The evidence for this in the rocks of the Jurassic Coast is clear; red sandstones with telltale characteristics of desert environments are overlain directly by clays, mudstones and limestones that were deposited in a marine environment. As if the nature of the sediments was not proof enough, fossils of marine animals are found preserved in these deposits. For millions of years desert conditions had prevailed; lakes and rivers had come and gone but the basic picture had remained much the same. So what happened to change this?

The answer lies with plate tectonics, the processes by which the distribution of land and sea is constantly changing, and which are responsible for building great mountain ranges and opening deep sea trenches. It was these processes that caused Pangaea to begin to break up at the beginning of the Jurassic. Rift lines began to develop where volcanic activity started to split the great continent apart, allowing the sea to flood in. The first stage was a roughly north–south split where the Atlantic Ocean began to form; this was followed by an almost east–west split which was filled by an ocean geologists have named 'Tethys'. The piece of the Earth's crust that was later to become Dorset and East Devon was on or around this split.

Of course, this still doesn't explain the general rise in sea level that is conspicuous by examining the widespread early Jurassic marine sediments. Why should the deserts 'suddenly' become submerged beneath shallow, tropical seas? Although the details are complicated, the general picture is quite easy to understand: as the great continent separated into smaller continents, more continental shelf was created, displacing the ocean and causing it to rise.

This may have been a fortuitous scenario for the development of life on the planet. At the end of the Permian Period, which preceded the Triassic, a great extinction had wiped out around 95 per cent of marine species. The break-up of Pangaea at the start of the Jurassic would have greatly increased the number and area of shelf sea environments, stimulating the evolution of diverse species. Dorset was one such environment and the record of the life in the Tethys Ocean is preserved in its cliffs.

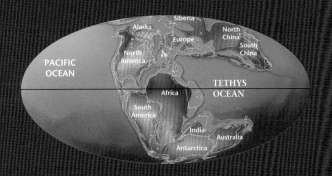

◄ *The famous Cobb and harbour at Lyme Regis.*

CHAPTER 2 | THE SEA RETURNS

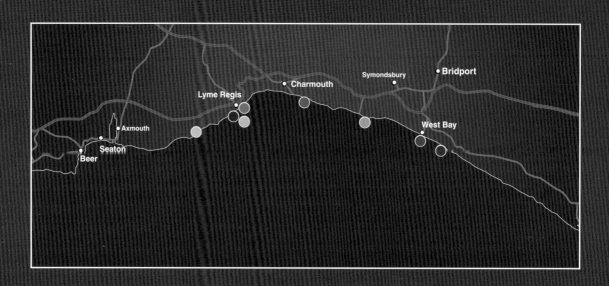

○ *Lyme Regis*
Page 30

● *Broad Ledge*
Page 33

● *Bindon Landslip*
Page 35

○ *Lyme Regis*
Page 37

○ *Cain's Folly, Stonebarrow*
Page 39

● *Golden Cap*
Page 41

○ *West Bay*
Page 43

○ *East Cliff*
Page 45

Crumbling cliffs on the east ▶
side of Lyme Regis.

LANDSLIPS

You may think that landslips are an unsightly and unfortunate feature of Britain's coastline, but they are nevertheless a key reason why the coast of East Devon and Dorset was granted World Heritage status. Landslips, particularly in the soft Lower and Middle Jurassic sediments, continue to expose more and more fossil remains of ancient life in this period. It is these fossils that have enabled scientists to construct a picture of how life evolved during this important period in Earth's history.

It is not difficult to understand how landslips happen. In many parts of the Jurassic Coast the sediments are in layers lying roughly horizontally or sloping very gently towards the sea. Rainfall soaking through the upper rocks reaches an impervious layer, typically clay, and cannot pass through. Thus the water pressure builds up at the junction between two layers and the weight of sediment above eventually leads to blocks of rock collapsing seawards.

Landslips happen all the time and eager fossil hunters listen out for news of them, knowing there will be plenty of fresh specimens to collect. However, they can be dangerous places and it is important to heed safety warnings if you want to collect. There have been a number of famous landslips on the Jurassic Coast. In March 1790 a great crack opened up behind Hooken Cliff between Branscombe and Beer and about 7–10 acres (3-4 hectares) of the Chalk slipped 200 feet (60 metres) into the sea. This dramatic event has resulted in a very picturesque stretch of coastline.

Between Axmouth and Lyme Regis lies the Undercliffs National Nature Reserve, formed entirely from landslips. On Christmas Eve 1839 there was an enormous landslide at Bindon that became famous nationally and attracted thousands of visitors. Today this is part of the Nature Reserve and has many special plant and animal species.

A landslip in the cliffs east of Charmouth.

Bindon Landslip
The great Bindon landslip occurred on Christmas Eve 1839. It is now completely covered by vegetation and has grown into an important habitat for wild plants and animals. Landslips are common in the soft clays and sands along this part of the Jurassic Coast and reveal many new fossils annually.

LYME REGIS

With its little harbour sheltered by the famous Cobb, its pretty beaches and winding streets, Lyme Regis is one of the gems of the Dorset coast. It is not an obvious place for a port, but there is little option between Exmouth and Weymouth, so it seems somewhere had to be chosen to serve the area's rich agricultural hinterland. The town first appears in documents in the year AD 774 and it is mentioned in the Domesday Book of 1086. By the thirteenth century it had become an important harbour and in 1284 was granted a royal charter by Edward I. In the sixteenth and seventeenth centuries Lyme Regis was a flourishing port, trading with Europe, Africa and Newfoundland.

Lyme Regis is situated on a part of the coastline that is continually being eroded and where landslides are common. Probably much of the medieval town has been lost to these processes. The relatively recent sea walls have retarded the erosion. The Cobb was only joined to the mainland in the middle of the eighteenth century and this has interrupted the 'longshore drift' of material west to east, resulting in the growth of Monmouth Beach (above the Cobb in the photograph).

In 1685 the Duke of Monmouth landed at the beach west of the Cobb that now bears his name and claimed the throne from the Catholic James II. The Duke was the eldest illegitimate son of Charles II and hoped for support from strongly Protestant England. A bloody defeat at the Battle of Sedgemoor the same year ended the rebellion and in the aftermath the infamous Judge Jeffreys hanged some of the rebels on Monmouth Beach.

On a gentler note, Lyme is well known as the birthplace of Mary Anning (1799–1847), the notable fossil collector who became world-famous for her stunning discoveries. She unearthed the first ichthyosaur skeleton and the first two plesiosaur skeletons ever found; many of her finds are now displayed in the British Museum. In 2010 the Royal Society ranked Mary Anning as third in the list of women who have most influenced the history of science. Today Lyme Regis is still recognised for fossil collecting and many specimens can be found in the debris from the cliffs of the Jurassic Blue Lias.

Ichthyosaur skull.

Lyme Regis

The historic town of Lyme Regis is, with its near neighbour Charmouth, the fossil collecting centre of the Jurassic Coast. The cliffs here provide an amazing catalogue of the evolution of life in the Jurassic oceans around 200 million years ago. There has been an artificial harbour here for hundreds of years and the town was once an important port.

THE GREAT UNCONFORMITY

The Great Unconformity is a major feature of the Jurassic Coast. It may not be noticed by the casual observer but once it has been pointed out it seems to demand explanation. At various points on the coast we can see tilted Jurassic or Triassic strata overlain by horizontal Cretaceous strata. This geometric anomaly has a long and complicated history behind it.

The rocks of the Jurassic Coast are all sedimentary; they were formed as eroded material collected on the bottom of shallow seas, lakes and riverbeds, or desert floors. The continual movement of continents and associated changes in sea level mean that an area that was the seabed can become land. The movement of the tectonic plates can cause the horizontal sedimentary layers to be folded; this is the reason we see tilted layers of rock strata. This 'new' landscape is gradually eroded and may eventually disappear beneath the sea again. A new cycle of deposition begins and the horizontal layers settle on the tilted strata. This is what has happened to the Jurassic and Cretaceous strata on the coast of East Devon and Dorset. The junction between the tilted layers and the horizontal Cretaceous rocks represents millions of 'missing' years when this part of the world was land and was being eroded. In East Devon the entire Jurassic sequence has been worn away, leaving Cretaceous strata lying directly on top of Triassic desert rocks.

Towards the end of the Jurassic Period most of southern England was above sea level; the only sedimentary rocks that were being formed were the Portland and Purbeck limestones, the latter in shallow lagoons that often dried out. The land continued to rise during the early Cretaceous Period, a process that lasted for millions of years. During this time much of the sediment laid down in the Jurassic seas was washed once more into the sea.

The Great Unconformity at Peak Hill, west of Sidmouth.

Cain's Folly, Stonebarrow
Stonebarrow, just east of Charmouth shows the Great Unconformity. At the top of the hill sits the Cretaceous Upper Greensand, looking somewhat orange due to iron staining. Underneath lie Middle and Lower Jurassic sediments, but the entire Upper Jurassic is missing. This was eroded before the sea returned and deposited the Cretaceous sediments.

THE FOSSIL RECORD

The 'fossil record' is a term that many people are familiar with. It is now widely understood that the rocks of the Earth's crust contain the remains of creatures that existed at various times in the planet's long history. These remains are usually found in sedimentary rocks that have been deposited in water, typically where sediment has slowly collected at the bottom of a shallow sea. Hard parts of animals – shell material and bone – can be preserved, replaced by a different mineral, or form impressions in the compacted material; more rarely, soft parts can also provide fossils. For any individual creature living in an ancient sea, the chances of being preserved as a fossil would have been remote, but over millions of years of geological time it has happened often enough to present scientists with a great deal of information about how life on Earth has evolved.

For a long time the only fossils known were from rocks younger than about 550 million years, the Cambrian Period. This seems to have been when animals developed hard parts that greatly enhanced the chance of fossil formation. Nowadays much older fossils are known, particularly as modern equipment has facilitated the discovery of faint images and impressions of microscopic soft-bodied organisms.

Fossils are of vital use to geologists in helping them correlate strata in different geographic regions. As life has evolved it has left a unique assemblage of fossils in a particular period. Thus two types of rock in different areas can be recognised as being the same age if they contain the same fossils. This helps geologists build up a picture of what conditions were like in these areas at a certain time.

Some animals are particularly useful as markers because they evolved very quickly, meaning that some species existed for only a relatively short space of time. Ammonites are one such group of animals. Their shells became more ornamented as time went on and the divisions between the chambers of the shell became increasingly complicated, leaving wonderfully intricate 'suture' lines that are often visible in fossils. These features are used by palaeontologists to study evolution and to successfully divide rock successions into stages.

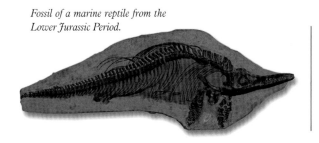

Fossil of a marine reptile from the Lower Jurassic Period.

Golden Cap

At 626 feet (191 metres) Golden Cap is the highest cliff on the south coast of England, thanks partly to its cap of relatively hard sandstone (the Upper Greensand). The cliffs between Charmouth and Golden Cap are frequently subject to landslides, revealing more and more of the fossils preserved in the rocks and helping to improve our understanding of them.

WEST BAY

Anyone who has visited HMS *Victory* in Portsmouth will have no doubt about the importance of rope to eighteenth-century ships. Much of this rope came from Bridport, which, since Roman times, has been an important centre for rope and net manufacture. The fields around Bridport were once planted with hemp for this industry, but now man-made material is used.

West Bay lies just over a mile south of Bridport and developed as a port for the export of rope. It is not a natural harbour, but one has been created by cutting a channel through the beach and digging out a small, square area. The present inner harbour dates from the 1740s but previous versions had existed for hundreds of years.

Cliff and beach erosion is a big problem at West Bay. The cliffs west of the harbour are of clay and suffer from mass movement caused by water penetrating, notably along fault lines. The east cliffs, too, are crumbling and the shingle ridge in front of them has been built up to alleviate wave erosion at the bottom.

The beach just east of the harbour has been reinforced with shingle from Burton Bradstock and is protected from the prevailing direction of the waves by the harbour walls.

West Bay is well known for the magnificent sandstone cliffs east of the harbour. These cliffs are formed from the Bridport Sands, a rock from the top of the Lower Jurassic and about 175 million years old. This sandstone may have been laid down in a huge delta that gradually grew southwards. The sandstone in the cliffs lies in horizontal layers, with harder bands sticking out at regular intervals. These harder layers contain calcium carbonate that has cemented the sand together. The calcium carbonate derives from the hard parts of organisms, and geologists have speculated that periodically a more unsettled climate resulted in an influx of shell material to the ancient environment. Thus the sequence in the cliffs here seems to represent some sort of cyclical sequence with the same pattern being repeated. We shall meet this again in the rocks at Kimmeridge (see pages 70 – 73).

The harbour at West Bay.

West Bay

The harbour at West Bay has been cunningly fashioned out of the mouth of the little River Brit, originally to serve Bridport's rope-making industry. The magnificent cliffs of Bridport Sands to the east of the harbour are a favourite with photographers as they glow in the evening sun. An important fault just west of the harbour means the cliffs here are formed of downthrown younger clays.

SANDSTONES

William Blake's 'Auguries of Innocence' begins with the words 'To see a World in a grain of sand…', suggesting that in something familiar and commonplace there is an intricate and beautiful story. His words were prophetic, because in sand we have something that is, in a sense, very representative of our world and the processes that have shaped it.

Many sand grains are made of quartz, which is a major component of granite, the most common igneous rock in the Earth's crust. When granite is weathered, the hard, durable quartz is not broken down chemically, only mechanically. It is washed away by rivers and streams, some of it ending up in the sea, where it sinks to the bottom, ready to form a sandstone. Some of it is built up by tidal action into beaches and sandbars across estuaries; some is deposited by rivers on land; some is blown about by wind in arid climates.

Sandstones always have a story to tell: it may be in the grains themselves or in the larger-scale structures in the rock. We have seen how current-bedding indicates a formation by seasonal desert streams or in wind-blown dunes. Well-rounded grains are also often an indicator of wind erosion. The grains may be cemented by calcium carbonate derived from living creatures which used it for their shells, providing evidence for the type of environment in which the sandstone formed.

There are many examples of sandstones on the Jurassic Coast. The cliffs in the picture are formed from the Bridport Sands, probably deposited by a huge river delta. As well as desert sandstones, there are sandstones that are marine in origin, such as the Upper Greensand, which is seen at Swanage Bay and at Worbarrow.

So, the next time you let grains of sand slip through your fingers, stop for a moment to think about the history of those grains. They may have gone through many cycles of deposition and erosion, have been in desert dunes, beaches, sandbars and on the bottom of ancient oceans, having first crystallised in a granite many hundreds of millions of years ago.

Sandstone cliffs at Burton Bradstock.

East Cliff

The dramatic sandstone cliffs east of the harbour at West Bay are formed from the Jurassic Bridport Sands, thought to have been deposited in a huge river delta. Note the regular spacing of hard and soft layers in the cliff. The harder layers contain more calcium carbonate, which has cemented the sand grains. The repeating pattern of strata is another example of cyclic sedimentation.

From Portland eastwards the Jurassic Coast is largely dominated by rugged limestone or chalk cliffs. The limestones all originate from the Upper Jurassic while the Chalk is Cretaceous in age. Conditions changed at the end of the Kimmeridgian stage of the Upper Jurassic and most of Britain became land once more, save for a large shallow lagoon in southern England. It was in this that the Portland Sand and later the Portland Stone were deposited.

By this time Britain was situated about 40° north of the Equator and the climate was tropical. This may seem odd but the world climate was a good deal warmer then. Fossil corals have been found of Kimmeridgian age in places that were as far north as 58° during those times. The Portland limestone is mainly a type known as oolitic (from the Greek word ooion meaning egg). These limestones typically consist of millions of tiny, spherical ooids, which are just visible to the naked eye and are formed on the bottom of shallow, tropical seas by the precipitation of calcium carbonate around sand grains or fragments of shell material. They are forming today on shallow banks around the Bahamas, a good indication of conditions that prevailed at the end of the Jurassic in southern England. Earlier in the Upper Jurassic another oolitic limestone had been deposited, the Osmington Oolite. This is well exposed in the almost vertical strata on the beach at Osmington Mills. This rock has spectacular trace fossils of worm burrows, shells and crustaceans.

The sea receded further during the last part of the Upper Jurassic when the Purbeck beds were laid down, resulting in a brackish, coastal lagoon environment. Some shelly limestones were deposited when the water level was relatively high and these have been quarried for more decorative purposes. Occasionally the lagoon dried out and polygonal desiccation cracks can sometimes be seen on the bedding planes, similar to those that are seen on dried out seasonal lake beds today. Remains of dinosaurs, early crocodiles, mammals and reptiles have been found in these rocks.

◄ *Durlston Head*
The Portland limestone cliffs of Durlston Head lie near the eastern end of the Jurassic Coast. In the bottom left of the picture is the lighthouse at Anvil Point, while just to the right of this are the Tilly Whim caves, where the limestone was once quarried.

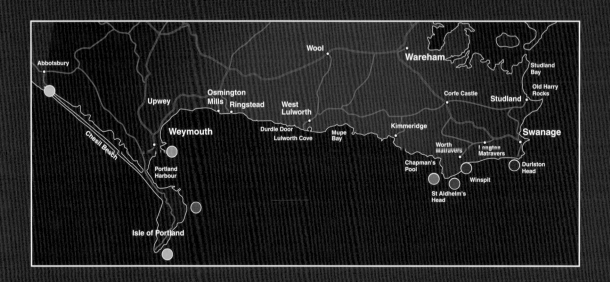

○ *Durlston Head*
Page 46

○ *St Aldhelm's Head*
Page 49

○ *Abbotsbury*
Page 51

○ *The Isle of Portland*
Page 53

○ *The Isle of Portland*
Page 55

○ *Weymouth*
Page 57

○ *St Aldhelm's Head*
Page 59

○ *Winspit*
Page 61

St Aldhelm's Head and the Isle of Purbeck. ▶

ABBOTSBURY

Abbotsbury is a picturesque village built from the local golden-coloured limestone. This is an oolitic limestone from the Upper Jurassic like the Portland Stone, but its iron content has given it a rich colour ideally suited to an ancient village in rolling Dorset countryside. Abbotsbury is surrounded by the remains of older settlements. On the hills and ridges to the north lie many Bronze Age burial mounds and even Neolithic monuments, while a little way north-west is Abbotsbury Castle, an important Iron Age hillfort taken by the Romans in AD 43.

In the Dark Ages Abbotsbury attracted the unwanted attention of Saxon pirates, who are said to have pillaged an early British church there dedicated to St Peter, and subsequently Viking raiders, who found the Fleet – the lagoon behind Chesil Beach – a convenient, safe harbour. However, things settled down when the Viking Canute became king of England. He granted land around Abbotsbury to his Saxon steward Orc, a Christian, who founded a Benedictine abbey here. The monks soon started a swannery to provide the abbey with fresh meat. The swannery has survived to this day, although the swans are no longer eaten!

Situated on a hill just outside the village is St Catherine's Chapel, built in the first part of the fifteenth century by the abbey. It survived the Dissolution possibly because of its importance as a marker for ships. St Catherine is the patron saint of spinsters and J.S. Udal, in his book *Dorsetshire Folklore*, records a custom where the young women of Abbotsbury went to the chapel on a certain day of the year and invoked the aid of the saint with the following prayer;

A husband, St Catherine,
A handsome one, St Catherine,
A rich one, St Catherine,
A nice one, St Catherine,
And soon, St Catherine.

St Catherine's Chapel built from the local oolitic limestone.

Abbotsbury

The village of Abbotsbury sits behind the western end of the Fleet. The small lane leading south from the village ends at the swannery, which is hidden by the shadow of the cloud. St Catherine's Chapel can be seen on the hill to the south of the village and to the left of the small lane. The Fleet is slowly disappearing as Chesil Beach continues to be driven landwards.

THE ISLE OF PORTLAND

The Isle of Portland has long been thought of as very different from the rest of Dorset, both by those who live there and by its neighbours. J.S. Udal, writing in 1922, tells us that the inhabitants of Portland 'say that they are Phoenicians, have never, until lately, allowed any English, or "foreigners", as they term us, to hold land in their territory, but have kept themselves a distinct people'. It is not difficult to see why this should be. Portland is connected to the mainland by only a narrow isthmus, it has a long history of stone quarrying with craftsmen who jealously guarded the secrets of their trade and in the last 200 years its development has contrasted sharply with that of its neighbour Weymouth, the archetypal seaside resort.

Portland is about 4 miles long and 1.5 miles wide and from a distance looks like a giant slab of limestone gently inclined to the south. In the northern part of the isle the limestone can be seen to be resting on the older Kimmeridge Clay. Portland was an important anchorage for ships of the Royal Navy for hundreds of years, but it was only between 1848 and 1905 that the harbour was created. This is one of the largest artificial harbours in the world and was made by building giant breakwaters of Portland Stone using convict labour from the prison. It played an important part in the First World War and was a major embarkation point for the D-Day landings in the Second.

Portland Bill is at the southern tip of the isle. A well-known geological feature here is the raised beach, which can be traced around the coast. The huts just above the old quarry workings on the eastern side of Portland Bill are built on it. A raised beach indicates a former, higher sea level and they are quite common features around the south coast of England. They generally date from the Ice Age, when the sea level fluctuated considerably between glacial and interglacial periods.

Old quarry workings on the Isle of Portland.

The Isle of Portland

The Isle of Portland is joined to the mainland by a narrow strip of land. Notice the light patches of former quarries on the northern part of the isle. The breakwaters of Portland Stone that create the harbour can clearly be seen just above Portland, while Portland Bill lighthouse stands out on the southern tip.

LIMESTONES

Limestone is a familiar rock. In the Cotswolds the golden-coloured stone has been used to create picturesque villages with thatched cottages where climbing roses perfectly complement the weathered limestone. In other areas, such as Portland, the limestone has a dull grey colour; it is an equally good, if not better, building stone, but the effect is altogether more austere.

Why is limestone so good for building? The answer is that, unlike some other sedimentary rocks, limestones have been cemented; this is what makes them hard. The cement is calcium carbonate or calcite and it precipitates out of seawater as buried sediment is gradually turned into rock on the seabed by the pressure from sediment above. This is not the case in all marine environments, only those where there is a relatively high amount of calcium carbonate in solution. Some of the calcium carbonate comes from lime-secreting organisms that used it for their hard parts, typically shells. At some stage in the evolution of life, some organisms developed the ability to extract the raw ingredients from seawater – calcium, carbon and oxygen – and use them to make protective hard parts. Thus limestone is an indication of a past environment rich in life.

Some limestones, such as the Chalk, are almost entirely organic: that is, they are composed almost completely of calcium carbonate. Others contain more terrigenous material: bits of sand, grit and clay eroded from the land and cemented together by calcium carbonate. There may also, of course, be fossilised shells, and some limestones consist mainly of broken bits of shell material bound together like the clinker left from a fire.

The cement we use in building is often made from limestone. Indeed, Portland Cement is well known, although nothing to do with Portland; the name comes from its resemblance to the colour of Portland Stone. To create cement, limestone is burned, which releases carbon dioxide, leaving calcium oxide or quicklime as the basic ingredient.

Portland limestone cliffs at Seacombe.

The Isle of Portland

View of Portland showing the quarries on the northern half of the isle. Huge quantities of Portland Stone, a strong oolitic limestone, were quarried here for building projects all around the world. At the very northern end of the isle, the right of the image, is Portland prison and it was convict labour that was used to build the breakwater.

WEYMOUTH

Weymouth is one of Dorset's premier tourist attractions, the ideal spot for a traditional English seaside holiday. Hotels and guest houses line the broad esplanade and the wide, gently shelving beach offers safe bathing.

The tourist industry is not, however, the reason Weymouth grew and developed in the first place. The limestone mass of the Isle of Portland has ensured the safe, sheltered waters of the bay, a factor not only in the origin of the settlement, but also in its more recent development following the decision to hold the sailing events here at the 2012 Olympic Games. The River Wey additionally provides a safe harbour. The first mention of Weymouth is in the tenth century and the ports of Weymouth and Melcombe Regis were recorded in the eleventh century.

These towns earned notoriety in 1348 as the entry point of the Black Death into Britain. It was in that year that a merchant ship from Venice, carrying infected rats, docked in Melcombe Regis. Weymouth's popularity as a holiday destination began in the latter part of the eighteenth century, when King George III decided it would be a good place to recuperate from an illness. He returned year after year, bringing with him an enormous retinue and ensuring at least a temporary prosperity to the town (by this time just known as Weymouth).

Much of the centre of Weymouth is low-lying, lower than most high-tide levels. Without coastal defences flooding would be a serious problem. The land on which Weymouth is built was originally a sandy spit on low marshland that had grown as a result of sediment transported from the north. This transport was stopped by the headland of Nothe Fort, prompting the growth of the beach. Naturally the spit and beach would retreat inland and the low-lying areas would be subject to periodic flooding. On the marshland behind the sea wall are two important nature reserves, Lodmoor Park and Radipole Lake, both home to many species of water birds and temporary home to many migratory birds.

The old harbour at Weymouth.

Weymouth
The tiny harbour in the centre of the picture, formed by the estuary of the River Wey, contrasts with the vast harbour of Portland at the bottom, protected by the artificial breakwaters. Nothe Fort, built in the latter part of the nineteenth century, stands on the southern tip of the estuary. The marshland by the river in the left of the picture is an important nature reserve.

SMUGGLING

In the eighteenth century excise duties were increased to pay for the spiralling costs of the wars with France. Coupled with the Enclosure Acts, which resulted in much common land, which sustained many rural communities, being enclosed and used by rich landowners, this had a devastating effect throughout the country. Many people in coastal towns and villages saw smuggling as the only way to survive. We may wonder how it was that many communities participated in, or at least supported, an illegal activity. First, for many of the rural poor, the crippling excise duties were perceived as deeply unfair and few would have seen anything immoral in depriving the government of some revenue. Secondly, it was a relatively risk-free enterprise; little manpower was available for its prevention and transport and communications systems in and around coastal areas were often poorly developed.

The Isle of Purbeck was heavily involved in the smuggling trade during the late eighteenth and early nineteenth centuries. Studland Bay provided a safe, gently shelving beach for small boats to unload their goods and the fine sand enabled barrels to be concealed for pick-up at a later time. The many caves and galleries along the rocky limestone coast excavated by the quarrying made ideal places to store contraband. It is likely that many of the quarry workers were involved and the 'whims' used to load stone would have been very useful for loading casks of tea and barrels of brandy. The villages inland were the control centres, as much organisation was required to store and distribute the goods safely and efficiently. Some time in the 1790s a large consignment of brandy kegs was hidden in the roof of the church at Langton Matravers. During a Sunday service the weight caused the roof to give way, killing one of the congregation!

There is no doubt that the geography and limestone geology of the Purbeck coast aided the smugglers' operations. Sheltered bays like Kimmeridge, Worbarrow and Chapman's Pool were ideal for unloading their luggers, while the headlands such as St Aldhelm's (see photograph) provided excellent lookout locations.

Smugglers hauled contraband by ropes up Gad Cliff.

St Aldhelm's Head

The dramatic promontory of St Aldhelm's Head. The Purbeck coast was popular with smugglers, who used the caves and quarries to hide contraband. The white cottages on the headland were originally coastguard cottages. The Coastguard Service was formed in the nineteenth century to combat the smuggling trade, which had grown enormously during the wars with France, when there was little manpower available to stop it.

BUILDING STONE AND QUARRYING

The massive beds of the Portland limestone have been worked to provide building stone for many centuries. Roman buildings in Dorchester show the use of Portland Stone, and in the thirteenth century it was being used further afield for projects such as Exeter Cathedral. On Portland it was mined on the coast and at opencast sites. The strata dip gently towards the south, ideal for cutting blocks and sliding them towards the sea to be loaded onto boats. The Portland Stone has been described as the best building stone in the world and there are a number of good reasons for this. It is found in massive (i.e. thick) homogeneous layers which, when combined with its hardness, make it structurally extremely strong. However, it is not so hard that it cannot be readily worked by hand, but is still hard enough to resist weathering.

Quarrying for Portland Stone in the nineteenth century was an important industry for both the Isles of Portland and Purbeck, where the stone also outcrops on the coast. In 1893 around 200 men worked 50 quarries on Purbeck, while the census of 1851 showed that, out of a male population of 2,143 on Portland, 480 were quarrymen and 33 were stonemasons. It is a testament to the skill of the quarrymen that, in an age of only limited mechanisation, so few were needed to produce impressive quantities of building stone.

Traditionally the stone was quarried by drilling a number of small holes, close together, along the desired line of splitting. Two little wedges known as 'feathers' were then put in each hole before a 'plug' was inserted between the feathers and struck with a hammer. As this is done in turn to each hole the rock splits along the line of holes. The quarrying was facilitated by the natural joints in the rocks. Joints are the result of tension caused by Earth movements and on Portland typically trend in a north-west to south-east direction. These joints also affect the continuing erosion of the coast and determine the shape and orientation of the many caves and gullies that are particularly noticeable on the east coast of the isle north of Portland Bill.

Old quarry workings on the Isle of Portland.

Winspit

Old quarry workings on the coast of the Isle of Purbeck at Winspit, south of the village of Worth Matravers. This was an important source of Portland Stone and was worked up until the Second World War. In January 1786 a ship called the Halsewell *was wrecked here in a terrible storm. Although 168 were lost, the bravery of the quarrymen saved many others.*

CHAPTER 4 | CHANGING ENVIRONMENTS

The Jurassic Period lasted a little over 60 million years, beginning around 200 million years before the present and ending about 145 million years ago. During this time most of southern Britain was covered by shelf seas: that is, the ocean above the continental shelf. It is in the shelf seas where life was concentrated, where light penetrates to the sea floor and a variety of habitats can be exploited. These seas were created as the supercontinent of Pangaea began to break up and geologists believe that throughout the period the global sea level gradually rose.

The period is divided into the Lower, Middle and Upper Jurassic, and these in turn are divided into a number of stages, all based on the assemblages of fossils, particularly ammonites. The rocks we see in the photographs in this chapter are largely from the Upper Jurassic, which comprises three stages, the Oxfordian, Kimmeridgian and the Tithonian. The origin of the first two is geographical; the Tithonian, unusually for geological terms, derives its name from Greek mythology. Tithonus, son of Laomedon of Troy, fell in love with Eos, goddess of the dawn, and the Tithonian heralds the dawn of the Cretaceous.

Sedimentation during the Upper Jurassic was controlled by a number of ridges and marine basins where circulation was limited and organic content high. Towards the end of the period, however, much of Britain was land with a shallow, salty lagoon over Dorset and south-east England. With such a diverse range of environments in such a small area it is not difficult to appreciate that the Upper Jurassic rocks of Dorset contain a tremendous variety of fossils.

The late Jurassic is generally thought of as the climactic period of dinosaur evolution with some of the greatest dinosaurs of all. Many would have waded through the coastal swamps of Dorset! Other types of animals were also around, such as crocodiles, flying reptiles and the first birds. Important fossils of these creatures continue to be found in the Upper Jurassic rocks of the Dorset coast.

◀ *Brandy Bay*
Tilted Jurassic strata in the cliffs of Brandy Bay below Tyneham Cap. The strata dip roughly northwards, being part of the Purbeck Monocline. This was the result of much later earth movements than those which resulted in the general west to east dip of the rocks of the Jurassic Coast.

CHAPTER 4 | CHANGING ENVIRONMENTS

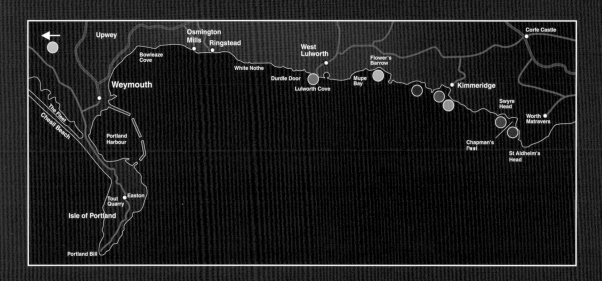

○ Brandy Bay

Page 62

○ The Lulworth Coast

Page 65

○ East Cliff

Page 67

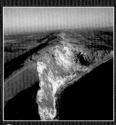

○ Flower's Barrow

Page 69

○ Kimmeridge Bay

Page 71

○ Kimmeridge Bay

Page 73

○ Houns-tout Cliff

Page 75

○ Chapman's Pool

Page 77

The beautiful concordant coastline ▶
around Lulworth Cove.

CYCLIC SEDIMENTATION

The sequences of rocks at some locations seem to repeat themselves; this can be seen at certain places on the Jurassic Coast where there are many strata, groups of which appear to occur again and again throughout the cliff face. It is particularly noticeable where there are harder layers at intervals in the cliffs, all of which seem to be of the same rock type, with similar layers of softer rocks in between. The cliff section between West Bay and Burton Bradstock and the cliffs at Kimmeridge show this particularly well.

Geologists refer to this type of pattern as cyclic sedimentation, meaning that the sediments have been deposited in a range of environments that repeated over time. It is not easy to correlate these sedimentary cycles with natural cycles; seasonal variations of climate clearly lead to variations in the sediment deposited in some environments, but the timescale involved is far too short. Many other factors that would cause the environment of deposition to change are not cyclical: for example, the movement of the tectonic plates of the Earth's crust. The sequence of rocks at Kimmeridge has been studied extensively and scientists have been able to suggest another possible cause of the sedimentary cycles there.

By studying what are thought to be similar sedimentary environments today it has been calculated that the sequences of rocks at Kimmeridge represent roughly 30–40,000 years for each cycle. This takes into account the amount of compaction of the sediments as they were turned into rock (see page 74). A natural cycle has to be responsible for this, and there is one such cycle that fits the bill. The tilt of the Earth's axis relative to its plane of orbit varies slightly over time, ranging from 22.1° to 24.5°: at present it is about 23.5°. This is known as the Milankovitch cycle after the scientist who discovered it. Such a variation would cause changes to the climate belts and might account for the rock cycles we see at Kimmeridge. See also West Bay, pages 42 – 45.

Cyclic sedimentation in the cliffs near Kimmeridge.

East Cliff
The wonderful sandstone cliffs of the Bridport Sands between West Bay and Burton Bradstock. The alternating bands of harder and softer sands indicate an environment of deposition that changed in a cyclical manner. The harder layers contain more calcium carbonate from marine creatures and that has helped cement the sand grains. Some have speculated that this shell material was brought into the environment by periodically stormy conditions.

FLOWER'S BARROW

The Chalk hills and ridges of Dorset are littered with signs of ancient civilisation. In particular there are many Iron Age hillforts occupying commanding positions and protected by steep ramparts. It is thought that each was ruled by a local chieftain and that the strong defences reveal a divided society where neighbours were often at war. This may have been a decisive factor in explaining why the Romans were quickly able to subjugate this part of the country, dealing with strongholds one by one.

Many of these hillforts have spectacular locations, but few can match Flower's Barrow overlooking Worbarrow Bay, where the Chalk ridge meets the coast. The ridge starts at the very eastern end of the Jurassic Coast at Handfast Point and runs westwards across the Isle of Purbeck. The layers of the Chalk dip very steeply northwards, so presenting a thin profile that, being more resistant to erosion than the softer sands and clays either side of it, forms the ridge.

Chalk is an ideal base for a hillfort. It is relatively strong and the ramparts are durable, yet it is not too difficult to cut and work. Good drainage means that rainfall quickly sinks into the bedrock without eroding the surface. However, water supply for the inhabitants of the fort was undoubtedly a problem and it is clear from such obvious practical difficulties that security must have been an overriding factor for its position.

Only about half of Flower's Barrow now remains; the rest has fallen into the sea and a semicircle of ramparts sits precariously on the edge of the cliffs. This gives us a crude but convenient measure of how quickly the Chalk cliffs are eroding, since the fort was constructed around 2,500 years ago.

A rather eerie legend is associated with Flower's Barrow. One foggy December night in 1648 several people reported seeing and hearing a large army marching over the ridge. The local squire sent word to the garrison at Wareham and soldiers were alerted. No more was seen or heard of the 'army' and the squire was summoned to London to explain the night's events.

Worbarrow Bay and the Chalk ridge with Flower's Barrow behind.

Flower's Barrow
Looking eastwards along the Chalk ridge from Worbarrow Bay. In the centre of the picture, at the top of the Chalk cliffs, can be seen the ramparts of the Iron Age hillfort of Flower's Barrow, or rather half of the ramparts can be seen; the rest have disappeared due to cliff erosion. The Chalk was formed in a very different environment from the largely deltaic Wealden deposits of the valley to the south.

OIL FORMATION

The exact process by which oil is formed is still unclear, but what is certain is that it is derived from organic remains which sank to the bottom of ancient oceans, typically single-celled planktons that collected on the beds of marine basins and were quickly buried. All living things contain much chemical potential energy; after death this is usually released through the process of oxidation. For the potential energy to remain trapped (and hence for oil to form) the organic remains must not be oxidised. This is achieved partly by rapid burial and by a lack of oxygen in the marine basin; the latter is often a result of the configuration of ocean currents. Gas and oil are generated after heating and compaction. The temperature at formation is less than 100°C, meaning a depth of burial no greater than a few kilometres.

The formation of the oil is only the first step in the creation of a reservoir of oil and natural gas. Because of its natural buoyancy oil will tend to migrate upwards through cracks, fissures and porous rocks. The oil will tend to saturate a porous rock such as sandstone by filling the spaces between individual grains. If such a rock is overlain by an impermeable rock the oil may become trapped, forming an oil reservoir.

The rocks at Kimmeridge from the Upper Jurassic contain strata with much organic content. It is these same strata, buried deep under the North Sea, which provide the important oil reserves. There have been attempts to make commercial use of the oil shales from the bay but the foul smell from them when burned ultimately led to this being unsuccessful. The oil well at Kimmeridge does not extract oil from the same strata but from older Jurassic sediments that are buried deeper.

Cross-section showing Kimmeridge oil source.

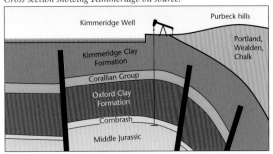

Kimmeridge Bay

Kimmeridge Bay with waves breaking on the Kimmeridge ledges – layers of hard limestone that are more resistant to erosion than the softer clays in between. The dark shales here have a high organic content that can lead to the formation of oil when the strata are deeply buried. The little oil well at Kimmeridge can be seen in the middle right of the picture; it has been producing oil since 1959.

KIMMERIDGE

The name of Kimmeridge is known to geologists the world over; it is one of a select number of places that give their name to a slice of geological time, in this case the Kimmeridgian stage of the Upper Jurassic. Such an honour is typically given to places where the rocks of a particular age are first described and where there is a complete and accessible outcrop of them (another stage of the Upper Jurassic is the Oxfordian). So the cliffs of Kimmeridge Bay are considered very important by geologists who study the Jurassic Period.

The rocks at Kimmeridge were formed at the bottom of quite a deep, tropical sea that teemed with life. Consequently the rocks here are rich in fossils that provide a wonderful record of life in the oceans around 155 million years ago. Apart from abundant ammonites and other invertebrates, many vertebrate fossils have been found here, including bones of dinosaurs, ichthyosaurs and plesiosaurs. A remarkable collection has been gathered by local resident Steve Etches, part of which is on display at Lulworth Heritage Centre. Earth movements had created a number of separate marine basins over the southern British Isles. Circulation was restricted in these basins and the stagnant clay that collected there was rich in organic material, hence the formation of oil deposits later.

Kimmeridge also has an interesting more recent history. In Iron Age and Roman times the hard, black shale was cut and polished to make jewellery. There have been a number of attempts to make use of the organic content in the oil shale. In the nineteenth century it was refined to make lamp oil, but it had such a pungent smell that this was quickly given up. In the sixteenth century a harbour was built to export alum extracted from the shale. Alum is the common name for hydrated potassium aluminium sulphate and was used as a fixer for dye in the wool industry. Today Kimmeridge is a marine wildlife reserve and is an excellent place for snorkelling and diving.

Kimmeridge Bay with Clavell Tower in the background.

Kimmeridge Bay

Kimmeridge Bay is carved out of soft Upper Jurassic clays with harder bands of limestone. Kimmeridge is a world-famous geological location and its cliffs have yielded a fabulous collection of fossils. Behind Kimmeridge the ridge is made of younger Portland and Purbeck limestones, which can be seen in Gad Cliff at the top left of the picture.

SEDIMENTARY ENVIRONMENTS

The rocks of the Jurassic Coast are sediments that gradually accumulated and were compacted to form hard rock. When we look at a cliff face we are seeing the results of processes that took place over many thousands if not millions of years.

Scientists who investigate lake and ocean floors today measure sedimentation rates in centimetres per thousand years (cm/ky). Obviously the rate varies considerably depending on the environment of deposition, but a slow rate would be in the order of a few centimetres per thousand years. As the sediment is turned to rock by the weight of sediment above, it is compacted many times. For example, consider a rate of sedimentation of 50cm/ky, compacted by a factor of 8. To form a rock thickness of 100 metres (330 feet) (with horizontal strata), a simple calculation gives a time period of 1.6 million years.

The rocks can tell us a great deal about what ancient environments were like. The type of sediment can be compared to that collecting in seas, lakes, rivers and deserts today. Structures caused by tides, currents and bottom-dwelling animals can all be recognised. The chemistry of present environments can be compared to the composition of ancient rocks and conclusions drawn about their formation.

Even the untrained observer can pick out clues to ancient environments. For example many people will have seen pictures of desiccation polygons on dried-out lake beds; well, look closely at the surfaces on the Purbeck limestones and you might recognise such features. They are particularly well displayed at Worbarrow Bay.

Desiccation polygons in limestone.

Houns-tout cliff
Looking westwards from Houns-tout Cliff towards Kimmeridge. Houns-tout displays a variety of rock types; at the bottom are clays which grade into sandstones and the cliff is capped by limestone. These rocks were deposited in very different environments.

ANCIENT GEOGRAPHY

Many people are fascinated by the idea of a time machine that would allow them to travel back to see what the world was like long ago, perhaps to witness mighty dinosaurs wading through forested tropical swamps with giant flying reptiles swooping on prey. At least today we are lucky enough to have computer-generated graphics which give us some idea of these ancient worlds. The evidence that guides these reconstructions has been collected from the rocks, and although some of it is accessible only via sophisticated equipment and expert interpretation, there is much that the average visitor can appreciate about the ancient environments in which the rocks of the Jurassic Coast were formed.

Coarse sediment is usually deposited quite near to land, so sandstone is often formed just off the coast or in a delta or estuary. We have seen how some sandstones are the work of desert lakes and streams and that these sometimes have the telltale cross- or current-bedding. Finer sediment – clay and mud – is usually carried further out to sea. The dark colour of some of these Jurassic clays indicates an environment poor in oxygen, perhaps due to a lack of circulation. Fossils give an indication of the environment in which the rock was formed. For example, oysters are found in some of the limestones on the Jurassic Coast; these creatures are still alive today and are only found in shallow water, fixed to the bottom.

At some locations we can appreciate how the environment changed over time. This is certainly true of Chapman's Pool, where the bottom of Houns-tout Cliff is composed of Kimmeridge Clay, from relatively deep water; this gradually changes to the sands of the Portland series, indicating a shallower sea; and finally at the top we have the Portland and Purbeck limestones, the latter formed in a shallow coastal lagoon which often dried out. Thus the rocks of Houns-tout can be read by the geologist to reconstruct how the ancient geography changed over millions of years towards the end of the Jurassic Period.

The coast around Chapman's Pool.

Chapman's Pool
The little cove of Chapman's Pool in Purbeck. To the left (west) of Chapman's Pool is Houns-tout Cliff, its height maintained by a cap of hard Portland Limestone. The cliff shows a varied selection of Upper Jurassic rocks, the Kimmeridge Clay at the bottom grading into Portland Sand and then limestone. This succession represents a variety of ancient geographies as the sea level and the pattern of the Jurassic coastline changed.

CHAPTER 5 | WHERE DINOSAURS ROAMED

In the picture you see the Dorset coast west of Lulworth Cove. Here the Portland and Purbeck limestones narrow to become a thin, steeply dipping strip that ends at Durdle Door, beyond which the Chalk takes over at the cliff face. Just visible at top left is Worbarrow Bay (see also later in the Chapter), beyond which the twin ridges formed by the limestones and the Chalk stretch away inland, with softer sediments in between. These rocks were formed during the latter part of the Jurassic Period and throughout the Cretaceous, the time when dinosaur evolution reached its peak.

Why are these rocks important to our study of dinosaurs? Why is this dinosaur country? The answers lie in the type of rocks we find here. While the Portland limestone and the Chalk are marine sediments and therefore unlikely to contain fossils of dinosaurs, sandwiched in between are the Purbeck rocks and the Wealden deposits from the Cretaceous Period, which are not marine sediments; they were formed in a variety of environments on or close to land. The Purbeck series of sediments was formed in shallow coastal lagoons, which occasionally dried out. We know that they were often freshwater lagoons from the fossil remains of freshwater molluscs which are still around today. The Wealden rocks were formed in large river deltas or in estuaries and lakes. These were the sorts of environments where dinosaurs thrived, wading through the shallow water and eating the vegetation or preying on other creatures.

At the eastern tip of Worbarrow Bay is Worbarrow Tout, formed from the hard Portland and Purbeck limestones. The side facing the bay is a good place to look for dinosaur footprints on the flat surfaces that were once the floor of an ancient lagoon.

◄ *Durdle Door*
The Purbeck coast around Durdle Door (centre of photograph). The rocks along the coast were mostly formed in a variety of non-marine environments which would have been inhabited by dinosaurs. They waded through coastal swamps and have left many fossilised tracks and footprints.

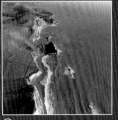

○ *Durdle Door*

Page 78

○ *St Aldhelm's Head*

Page 81

○ *Lulworth Cove*

Page 83

○ *The Fossil Forest*

Page 85

○ *Worbarrow Tout*

Page 87

○ *Worbarrow Bay*

Page 89

○ *Gad Cliff*

Page 91

The limestone headland of St Aldhelm's. ▶

LULWORTH COVE AND DURDLE DOOR

Lulworth Cove and nearby Durdle Door are two of the best-known and most visited places on the entire Jurassic Coast. The famous horseshoe-shaped bay of Lulworth Cove is a relatively recent feature geologically speaking, having been formed around 10,000 years ago. Its shape is easy to understand; a hard band of Portland and Purbeck limestones protects the entrance to the cove, while the soft Cretaceous sands and clays behind it are more easily eroded by the incursion of the sea. At the back of the cove the Chalk provides another more resistant barrier. The narrow entrance in the limestone ridge was probably formed partly by the sea exploiting a weakness and partly by a small river of seasonal meltwater. Again, the Purbeck limestone and the soft sands and clays formed in environments inhabited by many species of dinosaur.

Just to the west of the cove in Stair Hole is the famous Lulworth Crumple, a complex fold in the thin layers of the Purbeck series of rocks. It represents minor folding within the large-scale structure of the Purbeck Monocline.

Durdle Door, a little way west of Lulworth, must be the most photographed place on the Jurassic Coast. It is not difficult to see why: early-morning or late-evening sun transforms a picturesque landscape into a magical one. Durdle Door is an example of an arch, where the sea has eroded a gap in the Portland and Purbeck limestones and subsequently widened it. Eventually the roof will collapse and one side of the arch will become an isolated pinnacle or stack. Rocks to the west of Durdle Door are probably remains of previous arches. How does the sea erode the limestones? Basically it exploits joints which are planes of weakness in the rock. When layers of rocks are folded by great Earth movements (the rocks at Lulworth dip nearly vertically), the tensional forces often cause joints or cracks to appear in the rocks.

Lulworth Cove from the eastern end of the bay.

Lulworth Cove

In the centre of the picture is Lulworth Cove, backed by steep Chalk cliffs. The small village on the west side of the cove is built on the softer sands and clays of the Wealden series, while the Portland and Purbeck limestones form the cliffs and ridge along the coast. The footpath seen climbing the hill behind the village leads to Durdle Door.

THE FOSSIL FOREST

There are some visitors, often children, who express disappointment on first coming to the Fossil Forest, no doubt expecting to see huge trunks of stone with the pattern of bark clearly visible on the outside. Although such marvels are not on display, a little explanation should convince most visitors that this is a truly amazing and spectacular site.

The Fossil Forest is accessed from the coast path to the east of Lulworth Cove and sits on a broad ledge in the cliffs. The fossil remains are mainly large mounds of petrified algal growth called stromatolites. These algae colonised the stumps of dead trees and the hollowed-out centres of the rings indicate where the tree trunks were. The stromatolites are part of a steeply dipping layer known as the Great Dirt Bed, an ancient soil from the Jurassic around 140 million years old. It was one of the first fossil soils to be recognised by geologists. Some fossil wood has been found at the site and on the Isle of Portland several of the quarries have yielded good examples of fossilised tree trunks.

The trees were early varieties of cypress and juniper and probably inhabited large seasonal lakes and lagoons in a hot, largely arid environment. It is thought that the forest was suddenly flooded by saline water, probably the result of a rise in sea level caused by the Earth movements. The trees died and the salinity of the water increased due to the hot climate, helping to preserve the wood before it rotted. The stumps were then colonised by algae, which have formed the fossils we see today.

We can imagine these hot lagoons with tall trees and swamp vegetation as the typical habitat of some of the giant dinosaurs. The trees provided poor nutrition and the dinosaurs would have had to digest large quantities (see page 88). Perhaps the shallow water helped to support their colossal weight.

A stromatolite in the Fossil Forest.

The Fossil Forest
This is the stretch of coast between Lulworth Cove (bottom left) and Mupe Rocks. The cliffs are formed from the Portland and Purbeck limestones, while Bindon Hill behind is part of the Chalk ridge. On a small ledge in the cliffs just to the east of Lulworth Cove is the Fossil Forest. This section of the coast is within the army ranges and is only accessible at weekends and during school holidays.

THE STRUCTURE OF PURBECK

The beautiful Isle of Purbeck has a unique and fascinating geology. The rocks are from the last part of the Jurassic and the Cretaceous Periods. Two ridges of high ground trend east to west along Purbeck: the Portland and Purbeck limestones form the southern coast, while the Chalk ridge runs parallel to the coast in the north of the isle. In between lies the valley formed from softer sands and clays, out of which Swanage Bay to the east and Worbarrow Bay to the west have been formed.

Looking at the picture of Worbarrow Bay, it is not difficult to appreciate the structure of these rocks. The Chalk is the youngest of the sediments and the Portland limestone the oldest. All the strata here dip quite steeply to the north and are part of a giant fold known as the Purbeck Monocline. It is rather like a step, with the layers here representing the vertical part. Part of the step has been eroded, but further south on the Isle of Portland the almost horizontal limestones represent the top, horizontal part of the step.

A little more explanation might be necessary if you are familiar with the southern coast of Purbeck. Here the cliffs are peppered with disused quarries in the Portland Stone, which clearly lies in horizontal layers. It is not steeply dipping like at Worbarrow Tout or Lulworth Cove. A glance at a map should dispel any confusion; this part of the coast is further south and we are seeing the horizontal part of the step fold.

It can be very difficult to visualise the structure of the rock layers in three dimensions – it takes practice and a good imagination – but we can all recognise some of the features. As mentioned above, it is easy to pick out where the Portland Stone is in horizontal layers and where it is nearly vertical. Likewise, the Chalk ridge is relatively narrow because it dips steeply and we are seeing the ends of the layers. Since they were all laid down horizontally, something profound must have happened to them!

Horizontal layers of limestone at Winspit.

Worbarrow Tout

Much of the Isle of Purbeck has been captured in this picture, which looks eastwards from Worbarrow Bay along the valley that ends at Swanage. The steep, northerly dip of the strata can clearly be seen in the soft sands and clays of the bay as well as the Portland and Purbeck limestones of Worbarrow Tout at the southern end of the bay.

DINOSAURS

No other group of extinct animals has captured peoples imagination in the way that dinosaurs have; and quite rightly so, for these diverse and magnificent creatures dominated the planet's land surface for around 160 million years, from the middle of the Triassic Period to the end of the Cretaceous. The name dinosaur was first coined in 1842 by English palaeontologist Richard Owen and derives from Greek words meaning 'terrible lizard'. Animal classification is a complicated business, but basically the dinosaurs were reptiles which walked and stood with a more upright gait, rather than with their back legs splayed out sideways like most reptiles. This may have improved their breathing and hence their stamina when on the move. Thousands of species have now been recognised, many of them quite small creatures.

It is the giant dinosaurs that naturally generate the most interest, and some of them were truly enormous. The largest known from a good skeleton was found in Tanzania and was named Giraffatitan; it stood around 12 metres tall, over 22 metres long and probably weighed as much as 60,000 kilograms! Other fossil bones indicate that there were probably even bigger dinosaurs. Why did they evolve to such a large size? There are many advantages to be gained from size, but it may have been primarily a response to diet and digestion. The biggest dinosaurs were herbivorous and the world's plant life at the time was high in cellulose content and not particularly nutritious; the dinosaurs would have needed to eat large quantities of food and keep it in the digestive system for longer. The larger the animal, the more efficiently this could be done. The shallow coastal lagoons where the Purbeck series of rocks were deposited provided an environment where dinosaurs flourished. Many footprints of the three-toed iguanodon have been found on the exposed bedding planes that represent the ancient muddy floor of the lagoon.

Almost all species of dinosaur died out by the end of the Cretaceous Period, but it is now generally accepted that birds are their descendants, so the dinosaur lineage continues!

A dinosaur footprint in the Purbeck limestone.

Worbarrow Bay
A view of Worbarrow Bay carved from the soft sands and clays of the Cretaceous Wealden deposits. At the bottom left of the bay is Worbarrow Tout, made from the harder limestones of the Portland and Purbeck series. These rocks dip steeply to the north and dinosaur footprints have been found in the flat bedding surfaces of the Purbeck limestones.

TYNEHAM

If you want to know what life was like in an isolated rural community a hundred years ago, go to the deserted village of Tyneham. Now part of the army ranges, it is only open most weekends and during the school holidays. It was requisitioned by the army in December 1943 as part of the preparations for D-Day. The villagers left just before Christmas with the promise that once the war was over they would be able to return. This never happened: the Cold War ensured that military training remained a priority and to this day Tyneham is part of the firing ranges of the Lulworth camp.

Although it is a sad tale of wartime sacrifice, Tyneham has been preserved in time under army control. In summer a visit can be a memorable experience; there is ample car parking, you are free to wander around the village, which includes a museum in the schoolhouse, and stroll down to nearby Worbarrow Bay. The whole area is free from all commercialisation and it really is a chance to glimpse a lost rural way of life.

Worbarrow is a charming bay cut into the soft Cretaceous sands and clays, that are sandwiched between the Portland and Purbeck limestones to the south and the Chalk to the north. It was once a favourite place for unloading smugglers' cutters and the ruined coastguard cottages testify to government efforts to stop the illicit trade once the wars with France were over and sufficient manpower was available.

Worbarrow Tout is the conical hill at the southern end of the bay, separated from Gad Cliff by a low, narrow isthmus of land. On its northern side the flat 'bedding planes' of the Purbeck limestone are good places to look for dinosaur footprints. A little bay called Pondfield Cove has been eroded at a right angle to the concordant coast, visible near the top left corner of the picture. The origin of this cove is debated; it may be that the stream that flows along the valley from Tyneham once turned sharply south and eroded this gap in the ridge. If this is difficult to visualise we must remember that the shape of the coastline has changed relatively rapidly; it has been estimated that the rate of erosion of the coastline formed by the Wealden rocks may be of the order of around half a metre a year.

A row of cottages at Tyneham.

Gad Cliff

The deserted village of Tyneham sits between Gad Cliff and the Chalk ridge. Still part of the army ranges, it offers a unique insight into rural life in the early part of the twentieth century. Before then it was involved in the smuggling trade. Smugglers would land contraband at the foot of Gad Cliff for villagers to haul up with ropes.

CHAPTER 6 | MIGHTY DELTAS & CHALK SEAS

The Cretaceous is the most recent of the three geological periods that are represented in the cliffs of the Jurassic Coast. Although Cretaceous rocks are present in Devon and West Dorset due to the Great Unconformity, they are best displayed in East Dorset, particularly on the Isle of Purbeck. The photograph shows the Chalk at Ballard Down near Swanage, at the eastern limit of the Jurassic Coast. The Chalk ridge can be seen curving away into the distance, reaching the sea at Worbarrow Bay. To the left of the Chalk are the soft sediments from earlier in the Cretaceous, largely the Wealden Formation, while further left still the Portland and Purbeck limestones ensure that the land meets the sea with rugged cliffs.

The low, fertile valley between the two harder rocks is dotted with little settlements and at the eastern end is home to the bustling seaside resort of Swanage. There can be few landscapes where the relationship between scenery and geology is as clear as it is here.

Not only that, it is possible, through the rocks, to gain a clear picture of how ancient geography changed throughout the 75 million years of the Cretaceous. The period begins in the time when the Purbeck limestones were being deposited, another reminder that these divisions are based on the collection of fossils present, not on the rock types themselves. At this time Dorset was covered by shallow, usually freshwater lagoons. The Wealden rocks were then mostly deposited in a large river delta. We can tell this by the characteristic structures in the rocks, such as current-bedding that we see in river deltas today. Finally it becomes clear that the sea encroached once more and that coastal environments became covered by a shallow tropical sea, in which eventually the Chalk was deposited.

Notice, at Ballard Down, how the Chalk covers a much greater area than elsewhere along the ridge. This is because a large fault has resulted in the upper limb of the large fold (the Purbeck Monocline) being thrown down adjacent to the vertical limb.

◄ *Old Harry Rocks – Handfast Point, with the Chalk stacks of Old Harry and his family, is the most easterly point of the Jurassic Coast. The Chalk widens here because a fault has downthrown horizontal layers up against near vertical layers that form the ridge along the Isle of Purbeck.*

Wool

Wareham

Poxwell

Studland Bay

Osmington Mills
Ringstead

Corfe Castle

Studland

Old Harry Rocks

West Lulworth

Ballard Down

White Nothe

Flowers Barrow

Swanage Bay

Durdle Door
Mupe Bay

Lulworth Cove

Kimmeridge

Swanage

Swyre Head

Langton Matravers

Chapman's Pool

Worth Matravers

Durlston Head

St Aldhelm's Head

○ *Old Harry Rocks*

Page 92

○ *Durdle Door*

Page 95

○ *Bat's Head*

Page 97

○ *Gad Cliff*

Page 99

○ *Durlston*

Page 101

○ *Swanage*

Page 103

○ *Old Harry Rocks*

Page 105

Looking eastwards from Swyre Head ▶
towards Durdle Door.

THE CHALK

It is fitting that Chalk cliffs form the eastern end of the Jurassic Coast at Handfast Point. Chalk is the youngest of the rocks on the coast, formed near the end of the Cretaceous Period. It was deposited in a tropical sea formed as the Atlantic and Mediterranean began to expand. Areas that had once been land and the great river delta of the Wealden Formation were inundated and vast numbers of algae bloomed in the warm, clear waters.

Coccolithophores are algae that secrete tiny shields of calcium carbonate. They use around 20 of them as protection at any one time, constantly renewing and casting off used ones. These microscopic shields are wonderfully intricate; images of them made by electron microscopes look like works of art. Once discarded they sink slowly to the bottom, and in some parts of the world tropical seas are stained milky white by the millions of coccoliths on their way to the sea floor. This is how the Chalk was formed: billions of tiny coccoliths collected at the bottom of the Cretaceous sea, were compacted and eventually hardened into the brilliant white rock we see today. There is no better way to gain some appreciation of the vastness of geological time than to look at these mighty white cliffs and imagine how long it must have taken for them to form.

Something that has puzzled geologists about the formation of Chalk is the lack of other material in it. Parts of the older Chalk have some mud and sand but much of the Upper Chalk is almost purely organic in origin. This lack of terrigenous material is unusual, because shallow seas are close to land and therefore receive sediment from rivers and streams. The fact that Chalk has little such sediment has led some to speculate that the Chalk sea was surrounded by waterless deserts with few rivers entering it.

Chalk often contains nodules of flint, hard silica precipitated out as the sediment was being compressed and turned to stone. The silica originally came from creatures such as sponges that used it for their hard parts.

An electron microscope picture of coccoliths.

Bat's Head

The Chalk cliffs west of Durdle Door with the small promontory of Bat's Head in the middle of the picture. The undulating shape of the Chalk coastline is caused by dry valleys cut by streams when the water table was higher. Note the piles of rubble at the foot of the cliffs in the bottom right of the photograph, a reminder that erosion is causing the cliffs to retreat.

THE WEALDEN DELTA

The Weald is an area in south-east England, flanked by a ridge of Chalk to the north and south. The name is derived from the Old English word for forest and it is used to define a group of Cretaceous rocks formed near the beginning of the period.

Rocks of the Wealden group are found across southern England as far west as Dorset and east into parts of northern France. They are typically sands and clays that have been identified as having formed in a river delta. The size of the area over which these rocks are found perhaps gives a clue that this was no ordinary delta, but one formed by a mighty river. At times lush vegetation covered the delta and provided an ideal habitat for dinosaurs and other creatures. In Purbeck the Wealden rocks are found between two ridges of harder rock, the Chalk to the north and the Portland and Purbeck limestones to the south. The soft sands and clays form a rich, fertile valley that stretches from Swanage to Worbarrow Bay, thinning considerably as it does so.

The photograph shows Worbarrow Tout at the western end of the valley. Even from this height it is easy to see that the strata are tilted, dipping quite steeply to the north. They plunge underneath the Chalk but are above the Portland and Purbeck rocks to the south. The whole sequence is part of a major fold, the Purbeck Monocline.

Dinosaur fossils are relatively rare in the Wealden of Worbarrow Bay, but indications that this may have been the sort of environment they inhabited are not. Black lignite is quite common in some strata, the fossilised remains of ancient logs, branches and twigs from the Cretaceous forests where they once roamed.

The gentle curve of Worbarrow Bay.

Gad Cliff

The striking profile of Gad Cliff is due to the steeply dipping layers of Portland and Purbeck limestones. Note how weathered debris has formed an apron at the foot of the cliff. In the valley behind, cut out of younger, softer sands and clays, sits the deserted village of Tyneham. The whole area is part of the army ranges but is lovingly preserved and completely uncommercialised.

DURLSTON COUNTRY PARK

In 1863 Durlston was purchased by George Burt, a former stonemason from Swanage who had made his fortune in London, working for his uncle, John Mowlem (see page 102). Burt was the driving force behind the transformation of Swanage into a modern and fashionable town, he was instrumental in bringing the railway there. When he retired in 1886, Burt set about developing the Durlston estate. He commissioned a local builder to construct the Castle at Durlston Head, and planted trees and shrubs from around the world. Like another great Victorian philanthropist, Augustus Pitt-Rivers, Burt was passionate about learning and the natural world, and sought to encourage visitors and the local people to share his enthusiasms. He was responsible for bringing the Great Globe to Durlston. This unique monument in Portland Stone weighs over 40 tons.

Durlston Country Park was established in the 1970s and continues to fulfil George Burt's ambition to educate and enthuse people about the beautiful coastline's natural history. The website of the park neatly sums up the attractions for its many visitors: the 'amazing diversity of wildlife' in its 280 acres (115 hectares) includes over 200 recorded bird species, 500 species of wild flowers and 33 species of breeding butterflies. By carefully managing the wonderful natural resources, it 'has created a mosaic of nationally important wildlife habitats: sea-cliffs, downs, ancient meadows, hedgerows, woodland, and dry-stone walls – each with their characteristic plants and animals'.

In 1857 a local man named S.H. Beccles was determined to find out if mammals had existed at the time when the rocks of the Purbeck series were deposited. He therefore excavated a large pit on the cliffs above Durlston Bay, trying to find a stratum in which he believed a mammal jawbone had been found. As well as lots of reptile fossils Beccles found the remains of many small mammals. At the time the discovery was used by some as a vindication for the views of Creationists, who argued that it showed there was now no evidence for progressive evolution as mammals and dinosaurs had coexisted.

The Great Globe at Durlston.

Durlston

In the right foreground is Durlston Head with the castle nestled among the trees. The country park was the brainchild of the Victorian entrepreneur George Burt and was meant to encourage ordinary working people to appreciate natural history and geology. The Portland Stone was quarried in several places along this coastline, including at the well-known Tilly Whim caves at the entrance to the small dark valley on the left of the picture. Anvil Point lighthouse can be seen to the left of the valley.

SWANAGE

Like Weymouth, Swanage was a busy port before it became a popular tourist centre. In the early nineteenth century the town was at the heart of the stone industry. In those days the seafront was piled high with stone from local quarries awaiting transport to London or to great building projects elsewhere. Blocks were manhandled into small rowing boats and taken to larger boats moored offshore. It is hard to imagine how difficult and dangerous a job this would have been.

The development of Swanage as a popular holiday destination is due in a large part to two Victorian entrepreneurs, John Mowlem and his nephew George Burt. Mowlem was a local quarry worker who went to London to make his fortune. London was the capital of a great empire, and Portland Stone was the obvious choice for the construction of its grand new buildings and elegant streets. Boats bringing stone to London needed ballast for the return journey and this turned out to be some of the monuments that were being replaced. Today Swanage is littered with monuments and curiosities of old London, such as the Wellington Clock Tower. George Burt followed his uncle to London and subsequently took over the business. He became another great benefactor of the town.

Swanage sits on sandy Cretaceous sediments, largely from the Wealden Formation, between the Chalk to the north and the Portland and Purbeck limestones to the south. Durlston Bay, just beyond Peveril Point at the southern end of Swanage, is the type location for the Purbeck rocks and many important fossils have been found there.

The Chalk ridge that ends in the cliffs to the north of Swanage Bay was once continuous with the Chalk ridge of the Isle of Wight. North of this ridge ran the great Solent River, whose course roughly followed the present Solent north of the Isle of Wight; its upper course is represented by the River Frome. Following the rise in sea level after the last Ice Age (roughly 10,000 years ago) the valley of the Solent was drowned and the Isle of Wight separated from the mainland.

The lovely seaside resort of Swanage.

Swanage

The traditional seaside resort of Swanage lies in a broad sandy bay carved out of the soft Wealden beds between the Chalk cliffs to the north and the smaller cliffs of Purbeck limestone to the south. Swanage was once the centre for the export of Portland Stone, with the quay at the southern end of the town near the Victorian pier, which can be seen jutting out into the bay.

THE END OF AN ERA

At Handfast Point the dramatic Chalk cliffs stop abruptly and beyond stretches the vast expanse of Poole harbour and the low sandy cliffs of Bournemouth. This is the beginning of the Hampshire Basin, the geology of which is clearly very different from what we have seen along the coast of East Devon and Dorset. The rocks in the Hampshire Basin are classified as belonging to an entirely different era, the Cenozoic, as opposed to the Mesozoic which comprises the Triassic, Jurassic and Cretaceous Periods. This may seem an unnecessary use of geological names but the distinction is important, because the end of the Cretaceous is a momentous event in the history of life on Earth: it marks another mass extinction of species.

The Cretaceous extinction is thought by many to have been caused by the impact of a giant meteor. There are a number of pieces of evidence that have led to this conclusion, one of the most compelling being the so-called 'iridium layer'. Iridium is a rare metal and at a number of places around the world a thin clay layer has been found that is relatively rich in iridium. It dates from the very end of the Cretaceous Period. It is known that meteors are rich in this metal and the relatively high concentration in this layer could be due to the vaporised dust from a meteor that struck Earth, that dust subsequently settling in sediments. Further credibility has been added to this theory by the discovery of a suitably massive impact crater in Mexico that dates from approximately the right time.

However, some scientists think that an extraterrestrial explanation is not necessary. It is generally accepted that dramatic climate change was the primary cause of the extinction; the world cooled down considerably after the Cretaceous Period. It is the cause of the climate change that is debated. Some argue that volcanic activity associated with plate movement could have been the controlling factor.

Chalk stacks off Handfast Point.

Old Harry Rocks

The Chalk cliffs at the northern end of Swanage Bay represent the end of the Jurassic Coast. This is Handfast Point, with the Chalk stacks of Old Harry and his wife. To the right is Studland Bay, once a favourite anchorage for pirates. Note that here the Chalk lies in horizontal layers, whereas in other places we have seen that it dips steeply. The Chalk marks the end of the Mesozoic Era, comprising the Triassic, Jurassic and Cretaceous Periods.

CHAPTER 7 | OUR CHANGING PLANET

From a human perspective it is easy to imagine the Earth's surface as ancient and unchanging. However, we know that the Earth's crust – its outer, relatively thin layer – is constantly changing. The shape and distribution of continents are not fixed; they seemingly move around the Earth's surface.

In the last 40–50 years a new science has grown up to describe and explain this phenomenon; it is known as 'plate tectonics'. Many geologists were, at first, sceptical about this; they could not imagine how such a thing could happen. It soon became clear that, no matter how it happens, the evidence for it is overwhelming. Clearly, moving continents takes a huge amount of energy. At least the source of this is not a problem: we know that the interior of the Earth is hot; the deeper you go, the hotter it gets. This is clear from our mines, which only scratch the surface.

The interior is hot partly because our planet started very hot and is still cooling, but more importantly, heat is generated by the decay of radioactive elements. Geologists now think that huge convection currents are set up in the Earth's interior and that it is these that power the movement of the 'plates' of the Earth's crust. Volcanic and earthquake activity is mainly concentrated around the margins of these plates, where they collide or separate from one another.

Today, we can only really understand geology through plate tectonics. It explains why sediments that formed on the seabed are now part of the land, why rocks are folded and faulted and why fossils of animals that lived in the tropics are now found on our islands. It is a fascinating subject and the evidence for it is all around.

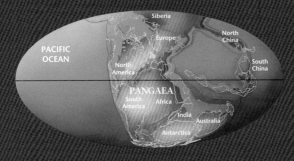 

◄ *Red desert sandstones along the East Devon coast.*

Pangaea
The two globes show the distribution of land and sea at the beginning and end of the Mesozoic Era. At the start, 250 million years ago, all the Earth's land was in one supercontinent (Pangaea), while at the end, 65 million years ago, this had broken up and the Atlantic Ocean had been formed.

CHAPTER 7 | OUR CHANGING PLANET

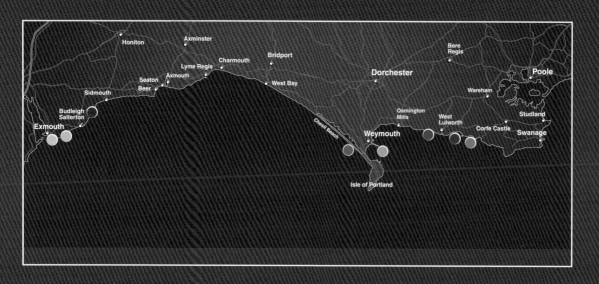

○ *Brandy Head*

Page 106

● *Brandy Bay*

Page 109

● *The River Exe*

Page 111

● *Straight Point*

Page 113

● *Chesil Beach*

Page 115

● *The Fleet*

Page 117

○ *Lulworth Cove*

Page 119

○ *Mupe Rocks*

Page 121

Kimmeridge Bay (top), Hobarrow Bay and Brandy Bay. ▶

CHANGES IN SEA LEVEL

Accounts of the geological history of the Jurassic Coast frequently mention changes in sea level. We know that much of the land surface is formed from rocks that were deposited at the bottom of the ocean and therefore that the distribution of land and sea has changed over geological time. The rocks of the Jurassic Coast seem to emphasise this. We have sedimentary rocks that formed on land, in river deltas, coastal lagoons, very shallow seas and quite deep seas – all in the space of 95 miles (155 kilometres).

There are many factors that cause the sea level to vary. On a global scale changes of mean temperature have an effect, since water expands as it warms. Water can be trapped on land in the form of ice, a reason why sea levels fell during the Ice Ages and rose again afterwards.

It is important to distinguish between local and global sea level change. Earth movements can cause regions to be uplifted or tilted downwards, meaning that locally sea level changes relative to the land. It can all get very complicated; indeed the notion of a global sea level is a difficult concept to grasp. Where is it measured from? Where is the datum line?

Whatever the difficulties, it is generally accepted that the mean global sea level rose from the beginning of the Triassic to the end of the Cretaceous Periods. This was probably due to the break-up of Pangaea and the creation of new oceans, which altered the volume of the deep ocean basins. Many of the changes in sea level recorded in the rocks of the Jurassic Coast are due to these global tectonic events.

The photograph opposite is a reminder of a relatively recent sea level change. It shows the start of the Jurassic Coast around Orcombe Point near Exmouth. The cliffs are formed of Triassic sandstones deposited in a desert. Beyond is the flooded valley of the River Exe. Such flooded river valleys are a common feature in south-west England and were formed as the sea level rose at the end of the last Ice Age.

Portland Bill has a well-known raised beach.

The River Exe
The River Exe joins the sea just west of Orcombe Point. The town at the side of the estuary is Exmouth, while at the bottom of the picture we can see a large holiday park. The estuary was flooded at the end of the last Ice Age as the sea level rose.

FAULTS – TENSION IN THE EARTH'S CRUST

The movement of the tectonic plates puts the rocks that make up the Earth's crust under tremendous strain, particularly where plates are colliding or sliding past one another. Rocks at or near the surface can react to these pressures by cracking or splitting; geologists refer to these as faults.

Faults that are the result of compression are often known as thrusts or thrust faults, where one layer of rock slides over another. Other faults are the result of tensional forces, perhaps due initially to compression, where strata have been slightly folded and the outer layers consequently stretched. One side of the fault usually slips down relative to the other side; these are known as normal faults.

There are many normal faults to be seen on the Jurassic Coast, a clear indication that the rocks have been involved in great Earth movements. In the cliffs look out for bands of rock that suddenly stop and then continue a little way above or below their previous level. Faults are lines of weakness and are often exploited by the forces of erosion. It is common for rivers and streams to flow along fault lines. Unusual breaks or protuberances in the coastline may indicate a fault. The picture shows the sandstone coast between Orcombe Point and Straight Point in East Devon. Notice how the headland of Straight Point juts out quite suddenly from the line of the coast. A fault here runs at right angles to the coast through the holiday park. The rocks to the left (west) of the headland have slipped down and are now on a level with harder sandstones which have proved more resistant to erosion; hence the sharp edge of Straight Point.

Movement can still occur even along very ancient fault lines (or rather planes) of weakness in the Earth's crust. This is usually what causes the relatively minor earthquakes experienced by the British Isles each year.

A small fault in the cliffs at Kimmeridge.

Straight Point

Orcombe Point, at the bottom left of the picture, marks the start of the Jurassic Coast. The cliffs are red Triassic sandstones and mudstones. On the right of the picture the headland of Straight Point juts out sharply at a right angle from the line of the cliffs. This feature has been caused by a fault which runs along the side of the headland through the holiday park.

EVOLUTION OF COASTAL LANDFORMS

It was the Scottish physician James Hutton who was perhaps the first person to realise, in the late eighteenth century, that the Earth was very ancient. What Hutton realised was that the surface of the Earth evolves, partly, by the slow, gradual processes that we see operating on the planet today. He understood that erosion and deposition are going on all around us, all of the time. Rocks are ground down, material is transported away by rivers and streams, and deposited elsewhere, often on the coastline in deltas and estuaries.

The energy in the oceans is a major factor in this cycle. Waves batter the coast, wearing it away, and at other places deposit the weathered material. Thus the Jurassic Coast not only gives us a record of the Earth's history in the 185 million years of the Mesozoic Era, it provides a living, working reminder of the processes that have shaped it.

The photograph opposite shows the eastern end of the Fleet lagoon. This is a relatively recent feature, geologically speaking, and is shallow, brackish water dammed behind Chesil Beach. Blocks of peat are periodically washed up on Chesil Beach which must have derived from a previous lagoon environment, over which Chesil Beach has since migrated; a graphic reminder of the evolution of coastal landforms.

The Jurassic Coast continues to evolve and while sea defences at such places as Weymouth and Lyme Regis will stabilise parts of the coast temporarily, the coastline we know will eventually vanish and the rocks of the cliffs will be recycled again. Although I have talked about 'slow, gradual processes', figures of how fast the cliffs are retreating at some places may come as a surprise. It has been estimated that at Kimmeridge Bay, where the cliffs are composed mainly of clay, they are retreating an average of 39 metres (128 feet) per 100 years, while the Chalk cliffs of Ballard Down are retreating an average of 23 metres (75 feet) per 100 years (according to Andrew Goudie in his 1995 book *The Changing Earth*). Clearly in the 65 million years since the Chalk was deposited there has been time for much change!

Durdle Door.

Chesil Beach

A view looking eastwards along Chesil Beach towards the Isle of Portland. At the top of the picture is Portland harbour, protected by its two artificial breakwaters of Portland Stone. The pebbles on Chesil Beach are larger here than at its western end, although it is a myth that they grade smoothly from west to east.

CHESIL BEACH

Our journey through geological time along the Jurassic Coast is interrupted somewhat around Abbotsbury, where the coastline is dominated by a relatively young feature, Chesil Beach. This storm beach reached its present form only around 5,000 years ago. Waves, driven by prevailing south-westerly winds, have pushed sand and gravel eastwards along the coast. This process is known as 'longshore drift' and its effect can be seen at other places along the Jurassic Coast: for example, the small sandbar partly blocking the mouth of the River Otter at Budleigh Salterton.

At the end of the last Ice Age, about 15–20,000 years ago, the sea level began to rise, eroding large quantities of sand and gravel from cliffs in what is now Lyme Bay. This was driven eastwards by the prevailing wind and waves, forming Chesil Beach. The beach may originally have been sandy, but old cliffs in East Devon and West Dorset, which had been stranded by falling sea levels in the Ice Age, now came into the grip of the sea once more and large quantities of gravel were eroded and transported eastwards, covering Chesil Beach with the shingle we see today.

An enduring mystery about Chesil Beach is why the size of the pebbles in the beach is small at West Bay and much larger near Portland. Intuitively, perhaps, we would expect the larger pebbles to be dropped first by the waves and the smaller ones carried further. However, it may be that the larger surface area of the smooth pebbles makes it easier for them to be transported by currents.

Storms have played a very important part in the building of Chesil Beach; this is when the waves have the energy to transport huge quantities of material. Although rare in human experience, on a geological timescale they are frequent. In 1824 a great storm struck the south coast of England and devastated the Fleet behind Chesil Beach. Fishing boats were carried right over the beach, and the village and church at East Fleet were destroyed; it was recorded that the water reached 9 metres (30 feet) deep.

Chesil Beach just west of Abbotsbury.

The Fleet

Chesil Beach, with the shallow waters of the Fleet behind it. Most of the Fleet is no more than 2 metres (6 feet) deep and it is brackish water. It is fed by streams but seawater also seeps in through Chesil Beach. The Fleet is home to many endangered species and thousands of migratory birds spend the winter here. In the centre right of the picture, by the shore of the Fleet, is Moonfleet Manor, now a hotel and famous as one of the locations in the novel Moonfleet *by J. Meade Faulkner.*

TILTED STRATA

The rocks of the Jurassic Coast are all sedimentary in origin, which means they were formed from the collection and compaction of the weathered debris of pre-existing rocks. This occurred in desert landscapes, river valleys and deltas and most often in the sea. Sedimentary rocks appear in layers because, as conditions change, different types of sediment accumulate that perhaps differ in colour or grain size. These layers are typically laid down in horizontal sheets and we can often see them in cliff faces.

In some places the layers are clearly not horizontal but slope or dip steeply, sometimes even vertically. These strata have been folded and tilted by compression that is a result of the movement of the plates of the Earth's crust. It is these movements that have largely been responsible for the diverse environments in which the rocks of the Jurassic Coast have been deposited. Such tilted layers of rocks are exposed at a number of locations on the East Devon and Dorset coast. In East Devon we see the Great Unconformity (see page 38) where horizontal Cretaceous layers lie on top of tilted Triassic strata. In Dorset, on the beach at Osmington Mills, Jurassic limestones are tilted almost vertically.

The best examples of tilted strata are perhaps to be found on the Isle of Purbeck. In the photograph opposite we see Lulworth Cove, where, at the entrance, the Portland and Purbeck limestones dip steeply to the north (left of picture). At the back of the cove the Chalk also dips steeply north, as do the soft sediments in between. To the south-west, on the Isle of Portland, the Portland limestone dips gently to the south. This is an example of large-scale folding: all we see are strata orientated in different directions in different localities. It is the job of the geologist to piece the geometry together.

Tilted strata at St Oswald's Bay.

Lulworth Cove

Tilted layers of Portland and Purbeck limestones form the gateway to Lulworth Cove. These rocks dip steeply to the north. It is not so easy to see, but the softer Cretaceous rocks behind the limestones also dip steeply, as does the Chalk at the back of the cove. These strata are part of a giant asymmetrical anticline or convex fold. All of these rocks were laid down originally in horizontal layers; huge forces have been responsible for folding and tilting them.

COASTAL EROSION

The coastline is always changing: erosion is a fact of life. It is one of the reasons why the Jurassic Coast is such an important scientific resource, as continued erosion brings more and more fossils to light each year. In some places it also allows us to appreciate the structure of the rocks more easily.

Consider the photograph opposite of the Dorset coast. On the right is Worbarrow Bay, with Mupe Bay on the left. Between them sits Arish Mell. It should be clear from the photograph that there are two bands of harder rock trending parallel with the coastline, the Chalk which forms the cliffs at Arish Mell and the Portland and Purbeck limestones on the far right of the picture forming the southern boundary of Worbarrow Bay. When strata run parallel to the coast in this manner the coastline is said to be 'concordant'. Together with the nature of the different rock types, it helps determine the shape of the coast. Notice that where the sea has eroded the band of limestone, it has scooped out the softer rocks relatively easily to form the two bays.

Naturally, where hard rock meets the sea cliffs will form, and where soft sands and clays meet the coast we can expect a low-lying coastline. This dictates where coastal settlements can develop. Swanage sits on the soft Cretaceous sediments between two headlands of chalk to the north and limestone to the south.

Wave-cut platforms are quite a common feature of coastal erosion. Waves striking the base of a cliff eventually cut a notch in the base. As this extends, the cliff may become unstable and collapse, retreating landwards. Over time this results in a flat platform at the base of the cliffs. This is happening with the Chalk cliffs west of Durdle Door, where the Chalk can be seen protruding through the sand of the beach. One of the chief mechanisms of wave erosion is hydraulic pressure, where water is forced into cracks and fissures by wave action and the rising tide, causing enormous pressures to build up and hence fractures in the rock.

A wave-cut platform near Durdle Door.

Mupe Rocks

This is the stretch of coast between Mupe Rocks at the bottom left and Worbarrow Bay at the top right. Notice how the soft sediments between the Chalk and the Portland and Purbeck limestones are being scooped out by the action of the sea. This is a good example of a concordant coastline, where the strata lie parallel to the coast. In this case the strata are steeply dipping.

GLOSSARY

ammonite *An extinct mollusc closely related to octopuses, squids and cuttlefish. Their fossils are very useful to geologists because they evolved rapidly.*

bedding plane *The junction between two layers of sedimentary rocks.*

calcite *The mineral form of the compound calcium carbonate.*

Cambrian *The oldest geological period where we find conspicuous fossils and the start of the Palaeozoic era. Lasted from around 540 to 490 million years ago.*

Chalk *A rock composed almost entirely of calcium carbonate derived from microscopic algae.*

coccolith *The hard calcite shell of a coccolithophore.*

coccolithophore *A microscopic algae.*

concordant coastline *A coastline where the structure of the rocks trends parallel to the coast.*

correlation *The process of matching strata of the same age in different locations.*

Cretaceous *The last period in the Mesozoic era, lasting from around 145 to 65 million years ago.*

cross-bedding *Inclined bedding planes in sedimentary rocks that formed in ripples or dunes either underwater or on land, typically in desert environments.*

crust of the Earth *The outer 'skin' of the Earth, thicker under the continents than under the oceans.*

Devonian *A period in the Upper Palaeozoic era, lasting from 416 to 360 million years ago.*

dinosaurs *An extinct group of reptiles with certain characteristic features. Birds are thought to be closely related to them.*

dip *The angle at which a layer or stratum of sedimentary rock dips from the horizontal.*

discordant coastline *A coastline where the main structures of the rocks trend in a direction at right angles to the coastline.*

extinction event *A relatively short interval of geological time during which many species died out, perhaps related to a global phenomenon.*

fault *A plane of weakness in the Earth's crust where some relative movement has taken place. Can be caused by tension or compression.*

folding *The deformation of strata by Earth movements.*

Ice Age *A period when a reduction in the temperature at the Earth's surface led to an expansion of the polar ice sheets and of continental ice sheets.*

ichthyosaur *A giant marine reptile that lived during the Jurassic Period.*

igneous rock *A rock that has cooled from a molten state.*

iridium *Iridium is a rare metal which is relatively more common in meteorites.*

joints *Planes of weakness in rocks, where no or little movement has occurred, typically caused by tension or compression.*

Jurassic *The middle period of the Mesozoic Era, lasting from roughly 200 to 145 million years ago.*

limestone *A rock largely formed from calcium carbonate from the shells of organisms or from chemical precipitation.*

longshore drift *The movement of sediment or beach material along the coast by the action of waves, in the direction of the prevailing wind.*

GLOSSARY

Mesozoic *A period of geological time, lasting from roughly 250 to 65 million years ago.*

metamorphic *A rock that has been altered by heat and/or pressure.*

mineral *A naturally occurring chemical compound.*

monocline *A step-like fold in rock strata.*

mudstone *A rock formed largely of compacted mud.*

oolitic limestone *A limestone formed mainly of tiny spherical grains of calcium carbonate called ooids.*

Ordovician *A period in the Lower Palaeozoic Era, lasting from around 488 to 444 million years ago.*

palaeontology *The study of fossils.*

Palaeozoic *The oldest of the geological eras from which we see conspicuous fossils. It lasted from around 540 to 250 million years ago.*

Pangaea *The name given to the continent formed when all the world's land was joined together at the start of the Triassic Period.*

plate tectonics *The study of the movement of the plates of the Earth's crust.*

plates *The Earth's crust is divided into a number of plates which move relative to one another, driven by heat from within the Earth.*

plesiosaur *A large, carnivorous marine reptile from the Jurassic Period.*

quartz *A mineral formed from the two most abundant elements in the Earth's crust, silica and oxygen.*

quartzite *A metamorphic rock formed by the action of heat and pressure on sandstone.*

raised beach *An indication of a former, higher sea level.*

rhynchosaur *A herbivorous Triassic reptile.*

sandstone *A coarse-grained sediment.*

sediment *Material that has been eroded and transported elsewhere. The term is often used to refer to a sedimentary rock.*

sedimentary cycle *A sequence of repeating sedimentary layers.*

shelf sea *The relatively shallow sea on the continental shelf.*

stacks *Isolated pinnacles of rock on the coast formed by erosion.*

strata *Layers of rock. On the Jurassic Coast these are always sedimentary in origin.*

stromatolite *Fossilised structures formed by the action of blue-green bacteria.*

supercontinent *At times during the Earth's history all land masses have been joined in one supercontinent.*

terrigenous *Refers to material derived from the land.*

Tethys *The sea that began to form as the supercontinent of Pangaea began to break up in the Jurassic Period.*

Triassic *The first period of the Mesozoic Era, lasting from around 250 to 200 million years ago.*

unconformity *A junction between two layers of sediment that represents an ancient erosion surface, indicating that deposition was not continuous.*

wave-cut platform *A horizontal surface along the shoreline created by the action of waves.*

Wealden *A group of sediments from the Cretaceous Period, largely formed in a river delta.*

SAFETY & FOSSIL COLLECTING

On the beach

- Always stay away from the cliffs.

- Do not climb the cliffs. Rock falls can happen at any time.

- Beware of landslides and mudflows, especially during or after wet weather.

- Always aim to be on the beaches on a falling tide and beware of the incoming tide, especially around headlands.

- Beware of large waves in rough weather, especially on steeply shelving beaches like Chesil.

- Please take your litter with you at all times so as to protect wildlife and maintain the beauty of this World Heritage Site for everyone

On the coast path

- Keep well away from the cliff edges and ensure that children and dogs are kept under control.

- Observe all restricted access and diversion signs – this is a changing and active coast. The signs indicate danger.

- Follow the Country Code.

HAVE YOU MADE AN IMPORTANT FIND?

Tell us about it by contacting the nearest visitor centre or the Jurassic Coast Trust on

01308 807000

Collecting fossils

- The best, and safest, place to look for fossils is on the beach where the sea has washed away soft clay and mud.

- Do not collect or hammer into the cliffs, fossil features or rocky ledges.

- Keep collecting to a minimum. Avoid removing in situ fossils, rocks or minerals.

- The collection of actual specimens should be restricted to those places where there is a plentiful supply.

- Only collect what you need – leave something for others.

- Never collect from walls or buildings. Take care not to undermine fences, bridges or other structures.

- Be considerate and don't leave a site in an unsightly or dangerous condition.

- Some landowners do not wish people to collect – please observe notices.

The West Dorset fossil collecting code of conduct

- This applies between Lyme Regis and Burton Bradstock.

- Collectors are asked NOT to dig in the cliffs without permission.

- Important fossil finds should be registered at the Charmouth Heritage Coast Centre.

- The full code is available from Charmouth Heritage Coast Centre or by logging onto www.charmouth.org/chcc

USEFUL INFORMATION

Coastal Visitor Centres

Charmouth Heritage Coast Centre 01297 560772
Chesil Beach Centre 01305 206191
Durlston Country Park, Swanage 01929 424443
Etches Collection 01929 270000
Kimmeridge Marine Centre 01929 481044
Lulworth Heritage Centre 01929 400587
Portland Bill Visitor Centre 01305 821050
Seaton Jurassic 01297 300390
Steamer Point, Christchurch 01425 272479
Studland Beach Information Centre 01929 450500
Swanage Museum and Heritage Centre 01929 421427

Tourist Information Centres

Axminster – Silver Street 01297 34386
Bournemouth – Pier Approach 01202 471781
Bridport – Bucky Doo Square, South Street................. 01308 424901
Budleigh Salterton – Fore Street 01395 445275
Christchurch – High Street.. 01202 471780
Exeter Visitor Info and Tickets, Dix's Field................. 01392 665700
Honiton – Lace Walk Car Park 01404 43716
Lyme Regis – Church Street 01297 442138
Ottery St Mary – Silver Steet within library.................. 07749 134870
Poole – Poole Museum, Poole High St 01202 262600
Seaton – The Underfleet.. 01297 21660
Sidmouth – Ham Lane 01395 516441
Swanage – Shore Road.. 01929 766018
Wareham - Discover Purbeck within library 01929 552740

Traveline

Public transport information 0871 200 22 33

SOME CENTRES OPEN ON A SEASONAL BASIS

For additional information please visit

www.jurassiccoast.org

or call Jurassic Coast Trust 01308 807000

Museums and Attractions

Abbotsbury Tourism 01305 871130
Allhallows Museum, Honiton 01404 44966
Axe Valley Heritage Museum... 01297 24227
Axminster Museum.. 01297 639884
Beer Quarry Caves 01297 680282
Bridport Museum 01308 458703
Dorset County Museum 01305 262735
Exmouth Museum.. 07932 609539
Fairlynch Museum, Budleigh Salterton........................ 01395 442666
Fine Foundation Centre, Beer .... www.beervillageheritage.org.uk
Langton Matravers Museum ....www.langtonia.org.uk
Lyme Regis Museum 01297 443370
Norman Lockyer Observatory, Sidmouth ..... www.normanlockyer.com
Portland Museum... 01305 821804
Royal Albert Memorial Museum, Exeter...................... 01392 265858
Russell-Cotes Gallery Museum, Bournemouth............. 01202 451800
Sidmouth Museum 01395 516139
Swanage Pier Museum... 01929 427058
Swanage Railway.. 01929 425800
Wareham Town Museum 01929 553448
Weymouth Museum... 01305 457982

Other Useful Contacts

Geological Information .... www.dorsetrigs.org.uk
....www.new.devon.gov.uk/geology
....www.dorsetgeologistsassociation.com
Lulworth Army Range Office
...........www.gov.uk/government/publications/lulworth-firing-notice
National Trust Charmouth.. 01297 489481
National Trust Devon 0344 8001895
Natural England (Information on National Nature Reserves).... 0300 0603900
South West Coast Path Association 01752 896237

OTHER PUBLICATIONS

Fossils of the Jurassic Coast

A new and engaging perspective on the fossils found on the Jurassic Coast, showcasing their extraordinary diversity through a wealth of stunning photographs and specially commissioned illustrations.
(220 pages) ISBN 978-0-9931107-1-9 **£9.95**

The Isle of Purbeck

This book guides the reader along the coast and explains the processes which, over a period of 160 million years, have produced an area that is both scientifically important and aesthetically beautiful.
Size A5 (128 pages) ISBN 978-1-907701-00-9 **£9.95**

Walks along the Jurassic Coast

The spectacular scenery of the Jurassic Coast World Heritage Site is enjoyed by many thousands of walkers every year. This series of books is soon to be extended to cover the whole of the South West Coast Path.
A5 (64 pages) **£4.95 each**

Official Guide to the Jurassic Coast

This must-have book about the England's natural World Heritage Site is beautifully laid out, easy to read and full of fabulous images and diagrams, all at a very affordable price. (64 pages)
ISBN 978-0-9544845-0-7 **£4.95**

These and other publications are available from outlets throughout the Jurassic Coast and online from www.jurassiccoast.org/shop

For wholesale enquiries contact 01308 807000 or orders@jurassiccoast.org, or go to www.jurassiccoast.org/books